To Malcolm,
Christmas 1980,
from Bill & Lis Pilcher.

IN THE WILD
with Harry Butler

IN THE WILD with Harry Butler

Published by the Australian Broadcasting Commission
in association with Hodder & Stoughton (Australia)
2 Apollo Place, Lane Cove, Sydney

Postal Address: GPO Box 487, Sydney, 2001

National Library of Australia card number
and ISBN 0 642 97442 X

Printed and bound in Australia by Wilke
and Company Limited
37-49 Browns Road, Clayton, Victoria

Typesetting by Photoset Computer Service
Pty Limited, Sydney
Text type 10 on 11 Zenith

Designed by Susan Kinealy

Associate designer: Howard Binns-McDonald

Stills by Kathie Atkinson

Additional stills by Tony Wilson
Barrow Island stills supplied by Harry Butler

Editor: John Taylor

CONTENTS

INTRODUCTION

I made these In the Wild programs with the ABC mainly because I felt that Australians needed to know a lot more about our wonderful wildlife and the threats to it.

Too many of us have grown up with the idea that the only interesting native animals are the funny or cuddly ones like the koala. That's fine if you're running a souvenir shop, but it's not much good when you're watching an infinity of evolution on the brink of extinction. Too many precious and beautiful life forms have a question mark against their future for us to be leaving the matter to chance. Public interest and concern is the best friend the environment can have, and there's room for lots more.

We took this continent from the Aboriginal people who for tens of thousands of years lived here without destroying the balance of nature. They treated it with reverence and understanding, and were one with the land and its life forms. Our own record is very different. I hope these programs, and future ones, will help to preserve just a little more of our heritage.

Programs such as these cannot be made without the help of a huge number of people and organizations. I have thanked them all individually but would like to particularly thank the ABC for making it possible, Kathie Atkinson for many of the superb photographs in the book, Joe Bignolo for some photographs of me in tight spots, my long suffering family and friends and most of all the TV film crews who went with me In the Wild.

It was a pleasant surprise to discover how many people really wanted to know more, and how many are concerned about the future of our native plants and animals. The number of letters to the ABC or to me about the program was the proof of this. Most expressed their growing awareness of the wonder of the Australian environment. This appreciation is leading to practical concern about what must be done *now!*

The programs are an attempt to show my feeling about the land and its wildlife; about the need to save *all* the ingredients of any area to preserve particular beauties; about the uglies, unloved and hated reptiles, and creepy-crawlies with their own fascinating part to play in the drama of daily life. Another aspect of the program is the concept that there need *not* be conflict between development and conservation; industry doesn't *have* to destroy the existing environment; enough thought, enough care and planning based on enough knowledge and we can have our cake and eat it too – if we are not too greedy!

Harry Butler

TROPICAL AUSTRALIA
The Constant Battle
Survival in the Wet

LAKE ARGYLE
The Changed Environment

BARROW ISLAND
The Living Laboratory
The Key to Survival
The Cycle of Life

GIBSON DESERT
The Killers
Some Survive
Death of a Waterhole

SOUTH WEST FOREST
Karri
Tuart
Jarrah
Wandoo

LAKE ARGYLE
the changed environment

This is Lake Argyle — it used to be the Ord River before the dam was built — a narrow herring-gutted river during the wet season, and in the dry just a chain of pools. The cattle on this country caused so much erosion that soil from the plains and the rich country washed out to sea every year in silt and mud. The government had this dam built for economic reasons. But with a tremendous amount of foresight they made the whole area a reserve for wildlife.

Some of the wildlife we've planted on the islands formed by the lake. Others are escapees from the flood.

Within the past five years it's had a chance to stabilise and sort out some of the problems. What is happening to the wildlife? That's what I'm looking at.

With the bitter lessons of the Aswan Dam in Egypt as a guide, many scientists and ecologists had expressed grave fear for the future of this area, because results of massive interference

by men are never predictable.

As the waters began to rise the West Australian Wildlife Authority asked me to join Ord Noah, their last minute program to save the wildlife.

Surveys had shown there wasn't much left. The cattle had eaten out the grasses, the wind had blown away the topsoil and when the rains came the whole countryside eroded and washed away down the river. Waterholes silted up and the wildlife vanished, except for a few species favoured by these new conditions.

The Ord Noah team rescued these survivors and placed them in selected areas, safe from the floods. Some weren't particularly grateful.

The trees below the main dam are the riverine habitat, five years old, just growing. One time we thought that the whole bank of the Ord would be a thicket of these trees. It hasn't happened, not yet anyway. We're not sure why, but probably because on the Ord the water level goes up and down with use. Here below the dam there is a constant flow and the silts coming out are dumped on the bank and there is a soil depth for the plants to take root in. Where the rocks come right down to the water's edge there's no riverine habitat. And in time to come, for the naturalist and environmentalist, it may well be that on one side of the Ord Dam we have one race of birds or animals, and on the other side a totally different race and they won't even interbreed because there is going to be that gap of the dam in between. It's just another one of those fascinating studies that you get here. Wherever you turn there is something different, something peculiar and unusual about this great drowned area of land man has made for himself.

Above: The river below the dam quickly establishes riverine habitat. Below: The shores of Lake Argyle support very few trees

Look at this: the crocodile nursery! Nice safe mudbank, Mum and Dad are out there somewhere, six or seven foot long, waiting for lunch.

These little fellows are much more fragile than they look. People think of crocodiles as being big, strong, prehistoric beasts, whereas in fact they're delicate and soft and cuddly. When they get giant size I guess they're not that cuddly. The rows of teeth are specially designed for catching and holding fish and one tooth locks into a groove in the bottom jaw. In some scrap he's broken the tooth. Now he'll grow it again. What I'll do is pull it out, swab it with a bit of antiseptic and then we can let him go.

There is some beautiful design for living in a crocodile. His ears have very good hearing, covering the entire range of hearing under and above water. His nostrils are a little bump right on top of his head. When he goes under water they close. His eyes have three eyelids, one transparent one that comes back across. He's got a built-in face mask as it were. Even the tongue, or what should be a tongue, is a block — a valve that closes the throat right off, so he can swim with his mouth open and not fill his belly up with water. And his legs fold back in. When he swims he just tucks them away. He swims with his magnificent tail. Of course, like most animals he likes having his tummy tickled a bit.

This is one of the fellows who's really advantaged by the flooding of the lake at the moment. While all this grass and stuff is growing on the edge there are hundreds of frogs and little fish, plenty of food for all these animals. It doesn't mean they're going to stay like that. Once these animals build up in numbers something that eats them is going to start building up in numbers. It might be goannas, it might be hawks, it might be pythons. They'll start to build up in numbers because nature is never static, it's always on the move.

Even before the dam was built, cyclones would cause huge log jams in the gap where the dam is now. An enormous flood would follow, sometimes as high as this water is today. That would replenish fertility, re-cycle nutrients. Of course, some animals would be drowned but most would survive by clinging to the top of trees.

These are Golden Orb Weavers. *Nephila* is their scientific name. The big ones are females, the little ones are males, waiting hopefully around for anything that the female may leave. The great big clusters are the eggs. The eggs have just hatched out and around each egg sac there are thousands of young.

Each will climb right up to the top of the branch, stand up on its back legs and throw out a long plume of silk and when the wind catches it, it will blow away. Maybe they'll end on a tree trunk in the lake or maybe reach the mainland.

They go up to 10,000 feet on the winds and spread all over the world. They have very strong webs, strong enough to catch and hold a small bird like a finch. You see why they're called Golden Orb Weavers – the silk is quite golden in colour.

The Brown Tree Snake or Territory Tiger is one of the species that's been bettered by the dam because he can swim and hunt in trees and everything has been forced up trees in the floods and so there's been lots of food for him. He tried to bite me when I got him. Couldn't reach me though — his fangs are in the back of his mouth. He likes to live in rock crevices because there are bats and mice, lizards, insects, frogs, all those sort of things. He can survive on an island or a single rock crevice for a whole lifetime and rely on the food that moves in. If he really gets stuck he'll use spiders or he'll just go without. I know these fellows can go for up to 18 months without a meal.

They have big eyes, with a long split pupil like a cat, for night-time hunting.

Australia, because of its age and isolation, has lizards representing all known groups except one. And all are perfectly adapted to their particular environment.

Here's a Water Goanna, one of the Racehorse Goanna group. This one is totally adapted for water life: in fact most people who see them think they're crocodiles. They've got all the characteristics of a crocodile: he not only has nostrils on top of his head, but like a crocodile's they close when he goes under water. At the same time the third eyelid comes across and closes, so it's like he's wearing a mask under the water: he can see through it, so it doesn't worry him in the least. Of course we've got the remnants of that third eyelid in the corner of our eye, that little fleshy piece is all that's left in our case. He's got a beautifully flattened body and tail because when he swims he doesn't use his feet — he just wags his tail from side to side and moves through the water. He is a fish eater mostly, but he'll eat birds and lizards and anything else that comes along. It's quite a common sight to see two or three of these and half a dozen crocodiles sunning together on a bank. He's got tremendous claws for climbing trees and if anything is up a tree, like a bird's nest, he can reach it.

This is one of the islands that we set up in Ord Noah. About 40 acres of rock and spinifex and the original vegetation. We set it up as a seed island, that is we took a balanced colony of euros, two males and seven females, and put them on this island. As far as we know euros need about 20 acres each and the question is what happens when you over-stock an island with an animal like a euro. Native animals don't deplete their environment, so they either die or they get out. This is the first time in five years that someone's come back to have a look.

What I want to do here is find out how many animals have survived on the island, what sort of grazing they've been doing and what erosion, if any, has taken place due to grazing.

This island is over-stocked by all standards and the old argument of pastoralists is that it's the 'roos and the euros that do the damage to the country, because they come in such big numbers. And conservationists say it's not so. This island is deliberately over-stocked. Our living laboratory.

What we've really got here is a natural selection taking place. The over-stocked euros are grazing out the things that they like and plants they don't like are proliferating. So now the animals that can eat those plants, like caterpillars, will build up in numbers and then something that eats them, like birds, will come in and a whole new ecology will build up on this island. That's how evolution works, that's how eco-systems work. It looks as though this sort of population is much too heavy: another year will tell the story. We don't know how many animals are left yet. Might be the original nine, they might've bred, there might be 20 here now. That's the next thing to find out.

Euro is an Aboriginal name for wallaroo or hill-kangaroo. We don't know very much about Australian wildlife but the euro is one that we do know about, because way back in 1955 the CSIRO and the Agriculture Department of Western Australia set up some trial experiments in the Pilbara, because the graziers claimed that the euros were destroying their land.

Sheep were brought to the Pilbara in about 1880, and the flocks built up into enormous numbers by selectively eating out the grass and not eating spinifex. It ended up with the spinifex taking over and this was added to by the fact that the pastoralists burnt the spinifex to get re-growth in the summertime. The euros, however, ate the spinifex so they were advantaged by this and, of course, the benefit of the extra water put in for the sheep. What we learned out of that 20-year study gives us some hope that we can reclaim the original grassland/spinifex balance.

On this island we set up a controlled experiment. So many euros, no competition from sheep, so will they destroy themselves or will they strike a reasonable balance?

Animals under stress develop new techniques for living. Of course there is the third alternative I suppose — they can swim across to the mainland — it's a fairly long swim and although they can swim they don't like it very much.

It's going to be very interesting to come back here in another two years and see just what's happened to this island with this sort of population pressure on it.

Before white man came to change the environment, Aboriginal men already existed here as part of the environment.

Boys would be brought here after a 24 hour fast. No food — just water and perhaps some narcotic like *pituri,* a native drug plant. When they were doped they were blindfolded and brought around this path.

Imagine! You hear the birds calling in the background welcoming a new day. You're terrified, you know the biggest thing in your life is going to happen and you're standing, blind, and suddenly the hands leave you and you're totally alone. And you open your eyes and see — spiritual men, the keepers of the country, the soul and being of the whole Aboriginal people. The Father of all with his spear-thrower and his stone axe and his wives . . . and all the good things they guard and keep and replenish for the people. The wild turkeys, dingoes, snakes, kangaroos, everything, all portrayed in this gallery. This is your introduction to manhood; and more important, this is where you learn your place and pattern in the whole ecology of this environment.

The Aborigines believed that everything had a place and a purpose and they built their life, their entire life, around changing themselves to meet the needs of their environment. The white man changes his environment to meet his own needs. When the Ord was built, 800 square miles of land was covered with water — the environment was adjusted to our needs.

The people who made this gallery are gone, their culture has gone too, but the land, the animals, the plants are still here. Their lesson is for us to learn from so that for all time we keep all the riches of this heritage.

TROPICAL AUSTRALIA
the constant battle

This is tropical rain forest, sometimes called jungle, one of the most complex environments you can find. In Australia it covers less than one per cent of our total land mass, and of that less than half is this sort of monsoon rain forest. It has existed in one form or another on the face of the earth for a hundred million years, perhaps longer, and is the well-spring, the source of most forms of terrestrial life.

Weird fungi proliferate in the collapsed understory and in turn provide food resources for other living organisms.

Most people come up here in the Dry, the good times. They marvel at it — it's wonderful, thousands upon thousands of buffalo and pigs, millions of birds on the waterholes.

Why am I up here in the Wet, the bad time? As a biologist I want to know what happens during the Wet. Where do all these animals come from and where do they go?

When the Wet comes the whole Top End becomes an enormous lake as the rivers flow out over the surrounding plains. The huge flocks of water birds are one of the spectacular sights of this fascinating area.

But it's the buffalo that's become the symbol of the Top End: an introduced animal that destroys thousands of acres through erosion and silting of waterholes. Wild pigs do the same, so these animals must be controlled if we are to save our native wildlife — like the magpie geese, totally dependent on these waterholes in the dry season.

The plains are open, easily seen habitats of the Top End, but the jungles are impossible to reach during the Wet. They're remnants from past larger jungles which have survived fire and changing climate, and with them have survived an enormous variety of plants and animals.

We find a land snail — a close relative of the snail that lives in your garden, and just like the snails in your garden they are hermaphrodites, they can be male and then female and then male again. They lay about 40 eggs at a time, which hatch just at the time birds are feeding their young.

Then there's a real jungle animal — the Flying Fox, the biggest bat in Australia. They feed at night like all bats, but these are a special group that don't have radar. They rely on their eyesight and that's why they have such big eyes. Because of their teeth and their claws they don't have a lot of enemies. The main one is the crocodile who uses their quarrelsome habits. Their camps are over water in these jungles, and the little fresh water crocodiles lie just underneath the camp. By and by when the bats start squabbling and fighting, one gets knocked off his perch and flops down to the water. Bang! He's gone — the crocodile's got him.

Flying Foxes do a lot of damage in orchards, but in the jungle they live on blossoms and wild fruits.

Here's a goanna — it's a Gould's Goanna, one of the biggest lizards that lives here. There are lots of different lizards here, skinks and geckoes, but the king is the goanna — a hungry, fast moving predator that has no hesitation in eating anything that moves — or even things that don't. A bit of dead meat is good tucker.

The sharp claws and teeth and the powerful tail make him a formidable opponent to most residents of the jungle. But the little things destroy him, the beetles and ticks, and he in turn becomes food for others.

There's the Spotted Green Tree Frog, a bit different from the ones you get in other parts of the country. When he gets really annoyed he oozes poison, a white sticky slime. If you get it on your skin, or in your eyes or on your mouth, it'll burn very badly. This gives rise to the old story that frogs give you warts. This tree frog can jump, but he prefers to walk mostly.

His main diet is insects, spiders and centipedes, and he in turn is food for owls, goannas and snakes.

Jungles are associated with snakes, and Australian jungles are no exception — our biggest ones are the 25 foot long Amethystine pythons in the Queensland jungles. This one is a common jungle snake — the Brown Tree Snake or Territory Tiger — he ranges from black and white to a brilliant orange and gold. A superb looking animal.

Tree snakes are wonderful climbers and eat birds, frogs and similar things.

This Shining Flycatcher has solved the problem by building its nest on a twig too thin to allow snaky access. That's the male on the nest. A brilliant bird, completely blue. His lady is quite different, tan and white mostly — much less spectacular.

You don't have to go very far in this country to find a different environment, and in this case it's the beach. It doesn't look like a beach — it looks like a battlefield, and that's exactly what it is. On one side is the jungle and on the other side are the mangroves and the tidal flats; in between, the disputed area — the beach.

Many animals have learned to use the best of both of these environments. Hermit crabs are marine animals, but they go into the jungle, fight the snails, and take their empty shells for houses in the sea. These are scavengers of the beach — and they're now learning to move into the jungle.

As a mangrove animal they learned to move backwards and forwards with the tides and get their food wherever they could find it.

People usually avoid mangroves because they're full of mosquitoes and sand-flies and mud and ooze. Not a great deal is known about them for these reasons, but they're full of fascinating life forms. The mangroves are the first stage of the land claiming the sea.

They actually build their own gardens. Their roots catch silt, debris and mud, which builds up around them and this in turn catches more debris and mud and so they create their own micro-environment. All along the coastline of Australia, in fact the whole world, this is happening — this fight between the sea and the land.

It's not the way of man to accept such constant change in nature. We try to understand the process, so that our own attacks on the environment never get out of control.

TROPICAL AUSTRALIA

survival in the wet

The unknown is always exciting and the most unknown part of this northern country is its wildlife during the Wet.

Roads are impassable, and off the roads even foot movement is unbelievably difficult. So very few people have studied the patterns of life in this country during the rainy season.

You could go for days in this country and see little, except unfortunate animals dead on the roadside. And yet, if you know where to go, animals are here. Everywhere there are animals, but not like it is in the Dry, when they are all brought together on the little waterholes and billabongs. Now they're spread out, breeding, ready for next season and dry times to come.

There's a Tree Goanna — adapted for living in swamps at this time of year when there's too much water. He's too open to his enemies, the hawks and other eaters, so he comes up into a hollow tree where he's quite safe.

See how fat his tail is! That's all the dry season's tucker to keep him alive. He can add a little to it, but it might take him eighteen months to get another meal. Many people make the mistake of thinking all animals have to eat every day, but it's not true. These fellows and others like them can manage on one meal a year.

The yellow throat is part of his protection, making him look like a Green Tree Snake, so his enemies tend to leave him alone.

West from Katherine, the flat savannah gives way to a series of rivers and steep escarpments which inhibit the movement of wildlife. There are few people here, but huge herds of cattle which compete with the native wildlife.

As the country changes there is a change in plant cover and we find things like palms — relics from wetter climates in the past.

Since these major roads have been sealed, high-speed traffic doesn't give any animal on the road much chance. Some people actually go out of their way to run over things like snakes. That's crazy out here — these things don't hurt anybody in this country! Usually if you slow down they'll move off pretty smartly.

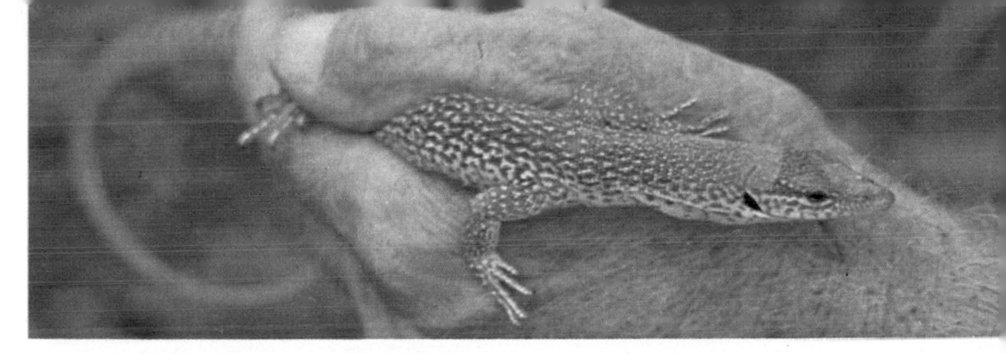

Here is a Frilled Lizard. The frill itself is a defensive thing and is used as a bluff, a scare thing. When the frill is all folded up neat and tidy, the animal can run through the bush easily and the frill doesn't hinder him. If he comes upon an enemy suddenly, he pops the frill, opens his mouth and there's this big scary monster peering at the enemy. That way he is able to protect himself by bluff.

This is the Victoria River. Rivers are the arteries that connect all of the environments of the Top End. I don't know how many Sydarbs are flowing down there — Sydarb is the amount of water held in Sydney Harbour, and as a measure of flow, it's the only one big enough in the Top End for the immense amount of water that flows away to the sea every year. Ten Sydarbs a day, 20 Sydarbs a day — and 18 farms: all that mud is running out to sea too.

At this time of the year these rivers are barriers, not corridors. Flying animals can get across them, but crawling, walking, wriggling, hopping animals get caught. All are forced to the cliffs; they have to go there because there is water everywhere else.

If you can get here when the rivers first rise, you can get a tremendous amount of information — animals caught by the flood are displaced and readily observed or caught. But once the first flood is past you've got to go up on the rocks where the survivors have found refuge. That's another reason why so little is known about this country during the Wet. Scientists and naturalists are mostly paid for results, so if you work a whole wet season and only get a little — it's not much encouragement.

The valleys with the rivers in them are the arteries of the country. The cliffs are wet weather refuge, but a whole host of animals live here, even in the driest, harshest times. In the wet season the valley populations move up into the cliffs and compete for residence and sustenance.

The most dangerous animal up here is the Death Adder. He appears small and insignificant except when he bites! Look at those huge fangs in that little head! The reason for this? He's a hunting animal. And because he's short and slow, once he digs in with the fangs he's got to hang on. He's got hollow fangs and a lot of poison, perhaps half a teaspoonful. When he bites, the whole lot goes in. A bad bite could kill a healthy adult in about three minutes. Poison glands are about the same as our spit glands and can make poison as quick as you can make spit. A really dangerous time for snakes is after they've been quiet for a long time and the poison is really strong.

The tail is interesting too. The Death Adder lies in a sort of S-bend and wriggles the tail spine. A bird or a lizard sees it, thinks it's an insect leg, dives on it and – he's gone. Snakes don't chew their food, but swallow it whole; they've got a marvellous dislocated jaw, which allows them to swallow things three or four times their own diameter. You don't find Death Adders very often, as they don't come out in the day time very much at all. He's out having a little bit of the sun – too much and he gets sunburnt. Snakes readily get sunburnt, and they can die from it.

Out in the bush snakes are not likely to affect people, and they have an important part and place in the pattern of the ecology. The only things I kill in the wild are cats and things like that, exotic species brought in by the white man. The things that belong here — like the Antelopine Kangaroo — look at them, enjoy them and leave them for somebody else to enjoy.

We really know nothing about what happens when these animals are forced together during the Wet. There's plenty of food and water, but enormous pressure on shelter and cover. So probably there is a lot more predation and less personal living space.

Things as large as the Emu have no worries anyway. They have powerful legs for kicking and a top speed of 60 kilometres per hour — they can outrun most predators found in Australia.

But smaller birds are less fortunate if they're caught napping.

If alarmed they sound a specialised call to warn of danger. By following the call a naturalist can often locate predatory animals in the bush.

A Green Tree Snake! No wonder the birds were excited! He's looking for things to eat! These are not dangerous.

Pity we can't have 'smellorama' — this fellow is protecting himself with stink. These ooze out a real stench. He can hear very well! That flickering tongue — that's listening, picking up air vibrations. The big eyes tell that he is nocturnal — comes out at night. The pupils enlarge, like a cat's at night. But unlike a cat's, this animal's pupils contract to a small round hole, while a cat's pupils contract to a slit.

When these cliffs were formed a great inland sea occurred in Australia. At that time there was a species of pigeons called 'Rock Pigeons': they had big spots on their wings and lived right across this northern part of Australia. When the sea came through it left one lot over in the east and one lot over in the west – it cut them off from each other and they became separate species. There were no pigeons left in the middle. And then the land reformed – and the pigeons from the east started moving west, while the western race moved east. Around the Victoria River they interbred.

In 1969 I helped collect the only specimens of these pigeons ever taken. On an expedition for the British Museum, we got six of them. Since then thousands of dollars and thousands of scientific man-hours have been spent looking around these cliffs for the pigeons – but they were never found again. It might seem strange to kill these pigeons. If they're so rare – why not preserve them? It's almost a paradox – you can't preserve something until you know something about it, and the only way you can know something about it initially is to collect specimens. What they eat, where they live, how they live, what their relationship with their environment is – all to be found out. Then, when you make a reserve you can make it with that animal in mind. So, first you collect, then you preserve environment – and that way you preserve the species.

There was just a chance I might locate it again and so I came prepared. That is why I carry a gun for the cats, which are probably the reason for the decline of the pigeons. The last time I was here I shot over 40 cats in two days. They were all along the cliff edges, killing everything that moved. It seems obvious that the feral cats have already done their worst – the pigeons may never be seen again, it's already too late. They're just another one of the species that have become extinct since the white man came to this country.

Think of the things we must still have and that can still be saved, if we respect the forces of evolution and conservation and creation; if we respect our environment and all the living things in it.

These immense tumbled boulders are the only gap in this entire range. The plants and the animals run into the barrier of the range, and stop. This in fact is the dividing line between western and eastern forms of wildlife. And these relict areas, where animals and plants meet, as it were, are most important to naturalists, scientists, and ecologists. In fact, important to everybody, because this is really where you find the whole essence of the heritage of Australia.

All of the animals which have ended up here against this barrier have come an immense journey: through evolution, through time and through space. This is their last chance against a major evolutionary change in this continent: the white man's intrusion, his flocks, his firesticks, his axes and dams.

They are too valuable to throw away, we've got to save them and the study of these places is essential for that.

To save a place you have to know what makes it tick and how it interacts. So study it. Then you can save it with purpose, and save it forever, because you know how to do it.

BARROW ISLAND
the living laboratory

To live in the desert you have to know all the tricks of the trade; how to survive with no water in sun, wind, and sandblast, with hungry animals all looking for you to eat. That's why I particularly like deserts.

Over half of Australia is desert; to most people this means lifeless wasteland, blazing, rainless heat. But most of our deserts are covered with specially adapted plants, which support a unique range of animal life. It's this marvellous wildlife that fascinates me — particularly here, because this is a desert island.

The Perentie is the biggest animal on the island that hunts in the daytime, except perhaps the Sea Eagle. It eats lizards and snakes, bandicoots, possums, anything that moves — it's a carnivore, not much smaller than the biggest lizard in the world, the Komodo Dragon, which lives off the north coast of Australia, near Bali. The Komodo grows to 12 feet but these only reach 9. Sharp claws on back and front feet, very sharp teeth and a long flogging whip tail all add up into a very formidable animal. When he's really moving he can do 100 yards in about 7 seconds — there aren't too many people who can do that, me included. But because they've got a three-chambered heart, when they've done the 100 yards dash their blood is recycling in such a way as to allow deoxygenated blood back through. They are exhausted and just run their head into a spinifex bush, where they are easily caught. My reason for catching him is to spray a colour code on his leg. These animals shed their skin and the paint comes off with it, so it's not a permanent marker, but we can get an idea how far they move in a given time.

Barrow Island lies 60 kilometres off the north-west coast of Australia. It's a low table of arid limestone and spinifex and supports the richest assemblage of wildlife found on any Australian island. It's existed for at least 6,000 years in total isolation. But in 1964 it suffered a blow that could have been fatal. Oil was discovered. Barrow oilfield has become the second largest in Australia.

In 1964 I did my first big study here, and found lots of new animals. When a report came out everybody got terribly excited about it. When the oilfield was declared, the Explorers' Club asked me would I do another study to see what the effect would be on all these wonderful animals.

That was in 1966 and I went up expecting the worst, but it wasn't so.

Wapet, that's the oil company that runs the island, had some very solid conservation measures: no pets, no firearms, no interference with the animals. But most important they had a restoration program started, because that's the key to conservation.

Barrow is really a living museum. It's a tiny piece of what the mainland was like before the white man came with his firesticks and crops and changed the whole balance of life. So important that as early as 1908 it was declared an 'A'Class reserve, and as such was one of the first in Australia.

To protect wildlife, you first have to protect the environment and the habitat. In this case it's the spinifex, or *Triodia,* harsh prickly plants that dominate the island.

Each bush balls into a round shape so that each leaf protects the others: that forms a pattern of shadow, which makes the interior of the bush much cooler and stops evaporation from the ground beneath. It looks pretty dead for food, but here and there on it are the seed heads just beginning to come out and the Euros chew the succulent end which is full of moisture and food. We're in the desert, where moisture conservation is very important. So spinifex is really a very important part of the country.

For instance when the wind carries dust and sand, spinifex acts as a trap, filtering the fine material down to help soil build-up. Other plant seeds get caught up, so when this bush dies there's a ready developed seed bed. This is what's called the Eyrean environment — a desolate, harsh, waterless, sunbaked area. Animals and plants use every possible way to survive. We call it a shocking place — nobody would want to live here really — but the residents can all live here superbly.

As a result of my studies on the island, the oil company asked me to become their Conservation Consultant in 1970, and at least four times a year I come back to make sure conservation measures are being carried out and to study and monitor the wildlife.

Euros are kangaroos especially adapted to living in arid areas. They're the largest animal on the island, and because they've evolved for centuries without threat from predators they show little fear of man. A lot of scientists have been here since the island was discovered in 1818, but in spite of all their work very little is really known about the wildlife. Every time somebody comes here something new or different is discovered.

If you travel on Barrow in the day you will see only one or two Euros. That's because everything goes to earth in the daytime and comes out at night. So that's when I do most of my work.

There is the Barrow Island Possum. See the big eyes — like most nocturnal animals — and the whiskers for feeling his way in the dark. He's even got whiskers on his wrists so he can feel as he's climbing without looking to see where he's going.

There's no shortage of volunteers, because the boys enjoy working with animals — and that's a key to conservation. Unless people care about it, knowledge won't save either the animals or the environment.

The Rock Rat is one of the small native rodents which live on Barrow. Although not a marsupial, it's a real Australian. It has chisel teeth just like any mouse or rat. Rock Rats have a delicate, tender skin — as a protective device. It's so delicate that if you touch the animal the skin breaks away in your fingers. When they are hunched up in a burrow or a clump of spinifex and a Children's Python makes a grab, the little animal can slip away: he loses a bit of skin, but he survives. They're so delicate and so tasty that bandicoots eat them like lollies — they just leave the skin turned completely inside out.

Workdays here begin at dawn and every day's a working day. Later it will get to over 130 degrees Fahrenheit.

Even the vehicles are part of the environmental program: they run on natural gas and cut out the pollution we would otherwise have.

There are over 300 oil pumps on Barrow. Nobody wants leaks to happen, because apart from the loss there's the damage to the environment: a big leak could destroy hundreds of acres. But even on a well run field you get the occasional maintenance leak from a cracked gland or joint, so there is constant checking and maintenance of the entire system.

The other thing about these pumps is the noise — it persists day and night, and one of my first problems on Barrow was that the noise might affect the animals and keep them away. But the animals actually use the plant for shelter and shade, and are quite accustomed to it.

Life in any desert is fragile and delicately balanced. We've managed to preserve this priceless living laboratory by understanding it. The miracle of its wildlife will continue, despite current use by man through his need for oil.

BARROW ISLAND
the key to survival

The Western Bearded Dragon is a small relative of the Australian Bearded Dragon. These island animals are even smaller. Like most of the dragon lizards they change colour with their feelings and in response to light and heat. Lizards tend to be fatalists: you can handle them and they'll just relax so long as they're not hurt.

I have yet to explore many of the Barrow Island caves. Some are very deep, going down hundreds of feet into the ground. All of them are used as habitat and for protection, places of safety for many of the animal species.

These caves are very hot and humid because of the water dripping through the limestone above, and stalactites and stalagmites are formed. So there is a bit of extra water for the animals, at least once in a while.

Humidity and moisture are the reasons why the animals live here; on the island, conserving moisture is a constant problem.

The animal which people usually associate with caves is the bat. Here there are Little Bats, *Eptesicus pumilis,* small insectivorous fellows which fly over from the mainland. They are quite big when their wings are spread out, but with them folded up they can fit into tiny crevices. Bats are mammals, and they secrete milk in the same way as goats or sheep or people.

Here we find the Rat-Kangaroo or Boodie — the whole area is a warren for them. They are omnivorous, with enormous front teeth and long, very sharp front claws for digging out insects and roots as part of their diet. They have typical kangaroo back feet — the split toe and the long central toe for kicking and fighting.

Some things arrive on Barrow by air, but most things come by sea on landing-barges. They're liable to carry rats and mice, so inspecting their loads is a necessary part of the problem of keeping Barrow Island an 'A' Class Reserve untouched by exotics.

An exotic is an animal or plant alien to the native environment — a thing that comes from somewhere else, like a rat or a mouse that doesn't live here naturally. These are the things we prohibit totally.

The birds aren't nearly so scientifically important as the island-bound mammals and reptiles. Because the birds fly, they can island-hop to lots of little islands between Barrow and the mainland, so we get lots of landbird visitors. Only six or seven landbird species are resident on Barrow.

Migratory birds stop in on the regular route from Japan and Siberia down to the Western Australian summerings, and then on the way back Barrow Island is a good motel for them. Seabirds bring the total to about 100 different species.

One reason there are so few resident landbirds is the lack of surface water — Barrow gets less than eight inches of rain a year. Oddly enough, this lack of water saved the Barrow Island fauna. No water meant no pastoral stock, while the native animals have evolved and can live without surface water. It's hard for some people to grasp that native animals can get their moisture from food and dew, and don't need to drink water.

Above: Young Brahminy Kite. Below: Singing Honeyeater Opposite: Black shouldered Kite

The Barrow Island Hill Kangaroos are Biggadas or Euros, and they're the lucky ones — they have a small pool of water and they hang around it all the time, since their survival depends on a permanent water supply.

In a hundred square miles of island there's one permanent soak. While there is free water, many of the animals will use it, but they don't need a lot provided they can replenish their body moisture. They recycle their own sweat, they recycle their urine, they seek shelter in anthills and caves and under spinifex bushes — and they even use the oil-rigs and vehicles if they can. They come out at night-time when the dew is on the spinifex and eat the damp shoots to make up a little bit more moisture.

Conserving body moisture is the whole basis of survival here — and at midday the only things that move are men: nothing else, not even the lizards. Men haven't learned these survival techniques because they don't need to. They can replenish their moisture all the time from the canteen — with cups of tea or perhaps stronger liquids.

This waterhole is the core of an area of about three miles around it. Animals will travel three miles, and so will various birds which need fresh water.

When the dry seasons come, all the animals which are totally water-dependent, like finches and doves, converge — the whole population of the island contracts to a little nucleus around the waterhole. If that pool of water were wiped out it would totally change the island's environment. Water is all-important.

The baby Children's Python has to watch out for its parents: in the snake world, you don't look after your kids — if you happen to run across them, you eat them. Many people try to put human interpretations on animal behaviour, but it doesn't work. Animal behaviour is about survival.

Isn't it amazing how snakes move? Three hundred pairs of ribs actually act like legs. Each pair of ribs has a scale between them. Three hundred pairs of 'legs', each one moving an eighth of an inch, add up to an awful lot of movement — plus the fact that the body moves sideways and pushes a little bit at the same time.

The most important habitat on the entire island is spinifex or *Triodia*. The low kind is habitat for lizards like the Spiny-tailed Goanna and small skinks, while the tall areas are the habitat for the mammals like the Hare Wallabies.

Meet a local — the Ringtail Dragon, a male. He is an insect eater — one of the many dragon lizards that love the sun and soak it up.

Above: Spiny-tailed Goanna. Below: Children's Python

Ring Tailed Dragon

Spectacled Hare-Wallaby

An oil-field needs gravel for construction, but a gravel pit means the destruction of habitat, often critical to the survival of animals. So we have methods of treating these areas to give full regeneration of the original habitat.

Regrowth is of two sorts. Some plants grow from seed coming on very quickly and replenishing the soil – they're colonising plants. Others come from root stock. When the bulldozers work, roots are left in the ground which then shoot again. So we have plants that are coming up from the original roots, and new plants that are growing from seed. A problem with regeneration is that the plants growing on this area are richer in moisture and nitrogen, and animals feeding on them get an additional amount of food. Many people think that giving animals more food is a good thing. In a closed environment like Barrow Island it can be very dangerous, and care must be taken that the regeneration program doesn't build up animals into a population explosion – because then we have exactly the same problem as not enough food.

We've got what we aimed for. Original conditions. And it's only possible on Barrow Island: because it's only 100 square miles; because we've got total control of the barges and aeroplanes coming in, and because the people here all work for us. Our restoration program evolved to suit these problems in this place – a desert island under specific conditions. If I had the same area on the mainland I'd have to come up with totally different answers to the restoration problems.

This very uninviting landscape grows on you, and eventually it really gets you because it's full of the most fascinating wildlife and we are going to keep it that way.

Above: 12 months' growth. Below: Original condition

BARROW ISLAND
the cycle of life

Previous page: *Planigale — the smallest marsupial on Barrow and in Australia*

The ultimate aim of conservation is balance — balance between the resources man needs and a respect for all other living things.

Here on Barrow Island we have some of the world's rarest animals — at least two species are thought to be extinct on the mainland. My job? To ensure that all these animals continue to live a balanced life, without destruction by man and his works.

I've been Wapet conservation adviser for the oil company since 1964. At one stage they asked me to join the staff, but I'd rather work as a consultant, because that way I don't have any conflict between what the company wants and what I have to do as a conservationist.

The island is unique. It developed over 6,000 years in total isolation from Aborigines and introduced animals and plants, which totally changed the mainland ecology for all time.

One way used by some animals to survive is the soak. Water caught in a sand-hill slowly trickles down and floats on top of the salt water. The Biggadas dig, exposing the fresh water table, and all the other animals that need water know about it. The doves and the bandicoots and the rat-kangaroos all drink here too. At night the whole area becomes a mass of animals, drinking while they can.

How does this fit in with animals' ownership of the areas? There are two concepts involved. One of them is *territory,* which belongs to an individual animal, and the other one is *range,* which is an area over which an animal can move and be tolerated by other animals. What we've got here is a whole series of *territories* that overlap, and their overlap is a common *range* in which all animals will tolerate each other. It's like people having their own house. If you bump into somebody in the street you may apologise, but you don't worry. But the moment a stranger comes in your *house,* that's your *territory,* it belongs to you and you object to people coming in unless you want them there. The *street* is your *range* — it's common ground.

In the same way here, all animals can come and drink, it's common *range* — like a street.

My early work here indicated the Euro was dying out. In 1964, when I first counted them, there were more than 200 animals but in 1966 and 1969, I was counting less than 50, and it looked very grim.

But at that time I didn't understand this range/territory situation. What happened was that I first counted after a cyclone when the animals were evenly spread all over the island, and got very big counts; later I counted in the stress times of the year, when the animals were all congregated on these few common ranges which were not involved in my count zones. Drawing conclusions on insufficient evidence is very dangerous. Now we know that the population of Euros on Barrow Island is quite stable although dynamic. I've got a secondary check. I pick up skulls of dead animals in caves, look at their teeth which tells the age at which the animal dies. There are no premature deaths, every animal reaches adult level. That means there are no problems for the Euros on Barrow Island despite the oilfield. That makes us pretty happy too, because our systems of conservation are working.

Although the dominant vegetation on Barrow is spinifex, there are over 200 species of other plants which are very important in the eco-systems. They have exactly the same problems as animals. They need protection against being eaten, protection against their competitors, and most of all, protection against the climate; the heat and the wind.

Take two different plants, *Corchorus* and *Sida*. Although they look different they both use the same techniques — a complete covering of felt-like fur across the leaves, and the young leaves stay closed up because they're succulent and tender and liable to lose a lot of moisture.

Right on the edge of the cliff, getting all the salt spray and wind, just growing in a crevice in the rocks is a plant with real problems. How does it protect itself? It has very few leaves and those few it has are covered with a dense mat of fur-like cotton-wool, so if an animal eats it it gets a mouthful of cotton-wool. It's also armed with a murderous set of spines — just touch them and they stick in.

When you live on a desert island things sometimes get a bit out of proportion. But the boys here haven't lost their sense of humour! By comparison with the spinifex these 30-foot trees are as big as giants, so they call this: 'The Valley of the Giants'. About 20,000 years ago mud and stone were washed down and deposited here: this is in fact a fossil valley. When it rains the water penetrates and all the year round there's water about 10 feet down. The long-reaching roots of the eucalypts tap the water table. These protect themselves against the elements with their leaves hanging so that the edge is towards the sun. They get minimal direct light on them, and there's minimal water loss. And to repel animals the leaves are coated in a waxy substance; if you break it, it's got a very strong odour familiar to every Australian — the smell of eucalyptus.

They don't look glorious, but on Barrow Island they support a whole range of life; honey eaters and insects come for the nectar flow. They in turn pollinate the flowers. The seed capsules play their part in the cycle of life and survival on Barrow Island. Most of them will be eaten, some will survive and continue the eucalypts in the Valley of the Giants.

Above: Corchorus *felt-like fur. Below:* Solanum *fur-like cottonwool and murderous spikes*

Below: Gossypium *— one of the most showy plants*

One mammal of a special interest is the Spectacled Hare-Wallaby. Once widely spread across the mainland, today it's very rare except for this thriving community on Barrow.

It is the main study animal and an ongoing research program is based on its capture and recording.

It's all part of the delicate fabric of life: plants and animals interwoven in a glorious net that has taken centuries to happen; and we can destroy it so easily. My job is to keep it, so that your kids and mine can see it all in all times to come . . . and enjoy it.

Big animals, little animals, plants — right down to the sea itself. We need them, not just for their own sake, but because all this has to be here for everybody forever.

There is no single, simple solution to the problems of continued existence for anything. Any answers are as complicated as life itself. Only one thing is certain: if we are to preserve our environment and save this priceless wildlife we need much, much more knowledge.

SOUTH-WEST FOREST

karri

One of the wonderful things about walking through the bush is that you never know what you're going to see next. Here it's one of the most delightful small animals you could get – Pygmy Possums. They really are delightful things.

You probably wonder why they're not running away from me . . . the reason is the blossoms they're feeding on have been in the hot sun and the nectar in them has fermented – these little fellows have eaten the fermented nectar and in fact they're drunk.

Many people think that this Karri forest in the deep south-west is the most beautiful forest there is. Probably because of the atmosphere, cool and damp, with the great boles going up supporting the sky.

It is almost like a cathedral in here with the winds moving over the top of the canopy, and down below in the undergrowth, the hush. Even the bird calls are muted. This is a monument — trees 400 years old, each big enough to cut two houses from — one of the biggest trees in the world. And they're found only in this high-rainfall south-west corner. All Karri forest is owned by the Forests Department and is a managed forest because that's the only way that Karri can be regenerated properly. This dense undergrowth, springing up in the shade and moist conditions, has a very wide range of jungle and indoor plants.

The lush greens, the wet moist conditions, and the ample fresh water are the things that really attracted the first settlers to this part of Western Australia. Can you imagine what it would be like? A fellow comes along . . . he's got a little block of land . . . he's fresh from England — he's raw. He's got a block of land in the Colonies and out he comes. He's got his axe over one shoulder, he's going to make himself a fortune. He's got to cut *that* down with an axe — no horse, no power saws, nothing! So they developed a specialised technique called ring-barking. They just went around the tree and took little bits out. One of our famous poets has a line . . . 'The stark white ring-barked forests, all tragic to the moon' — and it's so right, because you can look across this country and there are these great dead giants, marching in lines across the hills, and the little settlements carved out. It took tremendous courage on the part of the men who did it.

This sort of forest has two real habitats: one, the canopy which is the unbroken leafy part of the forest, and up there is a world apart . . . birds, animals, insects two or three hundred feet up in the air. You'd see them only with binoculars or something like that.

Down on the forest floor, the dense, lush undergrowth is the second basic habitat and there you get the small insectivorous birds, the slow or poor fliers who can hide and protect themselves in this vast green jungle. No hawks can penetrate here so they're relatively safe. And there's plenty of insect food on which they can sustain themselves.

Every forest has its ogre, its beast, its dangerous animal — and this is the one for here. This is Norne, the Western Tiger Snake, and he is not a very nice animal at all. He's one of the few snakes that — legend has it — will attack you on sight. You can see how wrong legend is. There probably is no snake in Australia which will attack on sight. If you happen to interfere with a snake by getting between where it's going or where it thought it was going or by some snaky reason you annoy it, then it may attack. But this Tiger Snake is out sunning in a little patch of the forest and is quite relaxed, although I'm alongside it. When I get even closer, all he wants to do is get away — then he gets mad because I'm deliberately annoying him. To catch a snake by the tail is always the best way, because when you've got them by the tail not many of them can climb up their own bodies. Even now . . . even though I'm annoying him very much, he's not trying to bite me. All he's concerned with is getting away.

The only safe grip for a snake is with your thumb and your finger under his ears — where his ears would be if he had ears. You can see why he's called a 'tiger' — a brilliant snake, lovely yellow belly and shiny black body. But he's the devil in this country; if that fellow were

to bite me now, without first aid treatment I could die in three minutes — so he's a very dangerous animal. Though he's only a small snake he's got fairly large fangs. They're not exactly retractile — they are on a bone plate that lies along the roof of the mouth. When he opens his mouth fully the bone plate tilts down and the fangs are extended forward. You can't see the fangs, just the tips showing through gum, which covers them. Instead of being hollow, the fangs have little grooves running down the front and the back. When the snake bites, this grooved fang goes into the flesh and the gum presses down around it, makes a seal and forces the poison in. Snake poison is a sort of saliva, a sort of spit, and the snake can no more run out of poison than you can run out of spit. Well, you can run out of spit — you can spit yourself dry and half an hour later you've got it again. At this time of the year these fellows are pretty poisonous because they've been through the cold wet months, lying dormant: they've built up their venom content and now they're hunting.

Tiger Snakes are readily told from all the other big dark snakes by the under-tail pattern which is completely single scales, right along under the tail. I mentioned the word Norne . . . that's the Aboriginal name and the Aborigines of this country very much feared this snake, and rightly so — he's a killer. When I let him go, he'll go straight into a crawl away — so much for the aggressive tiger snake. He's just not interested in eating me, he's much more interested in getting a little bit of sun and getting away from this horrible naturalist who's bothering him.

From the beast to beauty . . . and in the south-west forest there is a tremendous amount of beauty. Over six thousand different sorts of wildflowers, every conceivable colour and shape and size.

Above: Kangaroo Paw. Below: Cowslip Orchid

Donkey Orchid

Here's what looks like a bug eating a plant. But in fact that plant, which grows here in this swampy country where nitrogen is very low, makes up its nitrogen supply by actually eating bugs. It catches them and sticky hairs digest them, and so it builds up its nitrogen supply.

The most exciting of these insectivorous plants is deep in the heart of these peat swamps. They actually have the leaves converted into insect eating traps.

The leaf, even though it still carries out the normal function of leaves – it's green and can use sunlight to change raw material into food – is changed into a total trap. It has a little door, and inside there's some nice sloppy liquid which tends to smell a little bit. Round the top of it is a whole row of in-pointing teeth. This plant just waits in the swamp, the insects come along, attracted to the fluid, they crawl in to get to the fluid. The lid doesn't close like a trap ... it just stays like that, open. The insects trying to get out meet these down-hooked teeth. And eventually they drop back down into the fluid and they're digested. And the name of this wondrous plant is the Pitcher Plant, from its shape. There are pitcher plants of different sorts all over the world. In Australia this one is unique, the only one of its kind. It lives deep in swamps and has exactly the same problem as all the other insectivorous plants – how to get enough nitrogen. This is its way, it eats insects. An obvious choice.

Above: Drosera. *Below: Pitcher Plant*

These little streams are all the way through the forest – little tiny things, just trickles of water. By the standards of people from Europe or even the eastern seaboard of Australia they wouldn't even register as streams – they'd be gutters. And yet in these there are a host of fishes. There's the long, streamlined, beautiful shape of the Australian Minnow. He's got relatives in the South American zone and, of course, right across Australia and Tasmania. A good Australian Minnow will reach perhaps 6 or 7 inches. That beautiful streamlined shape, just like a salmon, is for hunting. He's an efficient hunting animal and he relies on speed to pick up midges and things like that.

There's a Night Fish: a sluggish, sullen fellow who lurks in the dark patches of the stream, comes out at night as his name suggests, and eats the little shellfish and insects like mosquito wrigglers. That's the fish I'm specifically looking for here — a really archaic fish. It's called the Mud Minnow, *Lepidogalaxius* . . . one of the first of the Galaxias, the father of the minnows. It's an ancient fish in that its spine, instead of ending up like a normal fish's spine, tends to branch out into bonelets rather than the rays of a normal fish's tail. This fish has a peculiar adaptation for living. He walks along the bottom of these tiny little streams — you can see those fins, you can see the way they fan out like legs: they're adapted for actually walking in the mud. When the dry season comes and these streams go down to little trickles in the moss, he walks up in those trickles and survives during the dry season. It's obvious to anybody who moves in this country that there are much bigger streams here . . . why do I come and fiddle around in these little poky gutters when there are really good streams of water?

The answer to that lies, again, in the European ancestry of our colonisers . . . because when they first came to this country and looked at these streams they found there were no good fish, from a fishing point of view. So they introduced Brown and Rainbow Trout. And these fish have pre-empted the entire river systems where they've been introduced. In Europe and the countries where these fish come from, the streams flow through fields and places where there's lots of stock and cattle, so there's lots of food in the streams. Here, there is very little food and the native fishes, these unique animals, get eaten out by the trout. The only refuge for them is in these tiny streams where the trout can't penetrate to get at them.

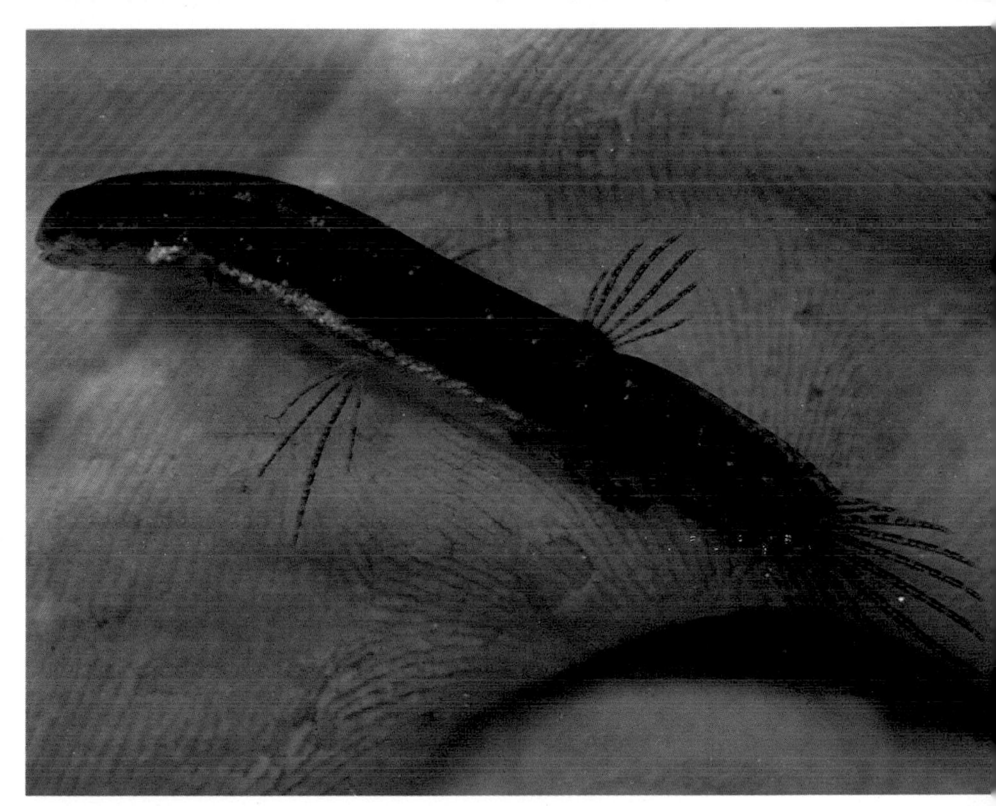

Above: Mud Minnow. Below: Black-striped Minnow

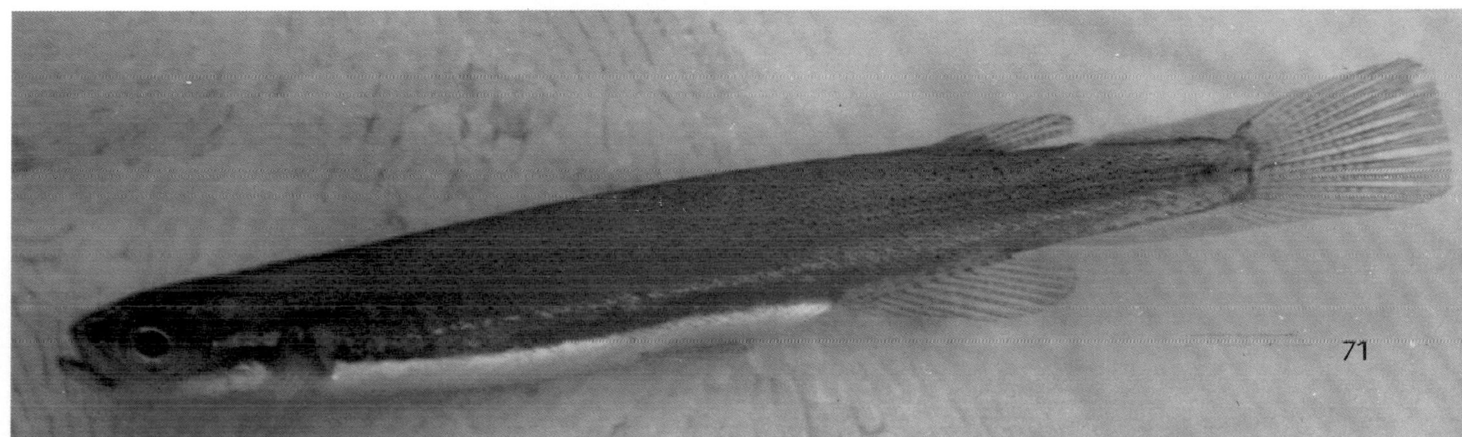

To the avid trout fisherman, this rock fall would be a marvellous place, but for me there's better sport than trout. In these streams is one of the finest opportunities for fishing in the world — the sport of marron fishing. It's the simplest thing in the world: all you need is a little bit of fine copper wire, a pole which you cut from the bush, a bit of raw meat tied to another stick, and most important, a marron licence so you can catch these delicacies when the season's open.

His eyes are on stalks and go back in under these very heavy overhanging ridges; he has a double pair of whiskers, one lot for coarse sensing across the bottom of the river, and the very fine ones for telling exactly where his dinner is. You've got a problem if you've got your eyes on the top of your head, and your mouth underneath with this great big thing in the middle: you've got a problem of finding where your mouth is! So when he's feeding in that position, those little whiskers turn down and tell his mouth where the food is. A beautiful animal ... threatened by the trout and by poachers and over-fishing. He's too big to be eaten by a trout, but they'll eat his little ones if they can.

Here we'll also find rats, but not the sort of rat you get in your house eating your goodies; this one is the bush rat, the South-west Bush Rat. They occur in the forest countries of Australia: beautiful little animals. I could track him down but this stuff's pretty thick in there. I'll set some traps.

And now, the morning after, here he is in the trap. Look at his teeth! He'd love to bite me! Contrary to what appears, the safest and best way to hold this animal is by the slack of his scalp, or the scruff of his neck, like a kitten. That way he can't reach me, and at the same time, he's not being damaged. If I hold him around the chest — it's so fragile, I'll collapse him inwards and he'll die.

In general appearance the Australian Bush Rat is very like the European, or Norway or Brown or whatever you like to call them . . . the introduced rats. There are a few obvious differences: the number of nipples is one; the introduced rat has ten to twelve young at a time — these have only four.

Next time you're in the bush and see a rat, let it alone because it's probably an Australian native.

When I let him go he doesn't waste any time getting away because all around there are crows, eagles, hawks — and on the ground lizards and snakes and all sorts of other bities and eaties, looking for a nice fat rat — because they're very good food indeed.

We also find the introduced rat. He's dangerous because he carries diseases, but from a naturalist's point of view he's dangerous because he replaces the native rats. He eats exactly the same food as them but at the same time he produces up to twelve young whereas the native rat only produces four, so he outbreeds everything else in the bush.

Combing his whiskers is an energy displacement thing — he's trapped — and just like a man who's angry in a situation where he can't do anything about it, he runs his fingers through his hair or claps his hands together. It's the same displacement behaviour — and rats display it very very obviously.

This is a rodent, a gnawing animal, and if one of his teeth breaks off this animal will die because the tooth grows right around and curves up and goes through his head — he stabs himself to death with his own teeth. That's if he doesn't die of starvation because his teeth block his mouth. The little paws are for digging — very powerful paws, much stronger than people imagine. And he has a little scent gland — that's how the rat marks his pathway: he owns a territory, and as he runs around the bush he leaves a little bit of rat smell, so if an enemy comes, he can run straight back to a place of safety purely by following smell. It's a territory marker, like dogs lifting their legs on posts; most animals have territory — even people put fences around their house as a marker.

All of these things — the birds and mammals, the fish, the frogs, the flowers — are tied to the Karri, this tree. And this tree will only remain while there's management. Management gives Karri and Karri gives you all the other things — sweet water, wildlife, the lot. A completely tied system in a forgotten corner of the continent where the brush of nature has swept past and a few little remnant things are left behind.

They can be saved for everybody if the trees are saved.

SOUTH-WEST FOREST

tuart

Everybody who comes to the south-west corner of Western Australia travels along this road through this particular eucalyptus forest. For me, it's a re-visit. Five years ago I did a biological survey here and it's going to be very interesting to see what changes and developments have taken place in those five years.

Tuart is only found in this south-western corner of the continent. Coastal limestones adjacent to the sea are the key to its survival, but you've got to get off the main road and into the bush to see what I'm looking for. And then you've got to get out of the vehicle because the noise of the vehicle spoils everything. Once you're out, the living spectrum of sounds, smells and sights — of life itself — makes the experience of just being here quite unique.

This is probably the most important forest on the coastal plain. It's called Tuart. It's not a terribly important timber but from a conservationist's and naturalist's point of view it's important because it's a forest won back from the developers. When this colony was first settled, one of the first areas to be taken up was this vast Busselton area. It was called 'Cattle Chosen' because cattle escaped from the first settlers and chose their own pastures in this natural grassland under the Tuart forest. It was already cleared: just big sticks of Tuart, a few little copses of peppermint understory and the rest was grassland — and so it became very useful; no extra work . . . you just put your cattle in and that was that.

At the time of Federation, when Australia first became a nation, one of the first things they decided on as a nation was a forest policy. And some wise person in those times suddenly realised there was no Tuart forest available. The then Premier of Western Australia, Sir John Forrest, gave back part of his land holdings in this area to form this Tuart forest. And for many years it was managed as though it was a farm. They grazed cattle through it, and burnt it every so often, but because the cattle kept the grass down they didn't have to burn very often. Then it was discovered there were no young Tuarts; the whole forest consisted of big trees. A very intensive research program was set up to find out what makes Tuarts grow. The answer: burning. All of the dead timber and the understory is scraped up and burnt at the right time; the seeds come down from the canopy into the ash bed, and when the rains come, up comes a stand of Tuart. You can often see the way the Tuarts have formed along an old ash bed. Where the canopy is taken away the peppermint comes in and that's a very important understory, because the peppermint is very dense and thick and provides shelter for certain species, like the ring-tailed possum, small birds and things like that. They can't live up in trees, but they can live in the understory. In the open spaces the peppermint forms full height copse, full forests in themselves. Peppermint's not a eucalypt – it's a plant called *Agonis* – and it gets its name from the strong pepperminty smell – the smell of peppermint and the smell of honey are forever in the air in this forest. And it's the honey and the blossom and the trees which provide all the various places where things can live.

Above: Rainbow Bird. Below: Female Rufous Whistler

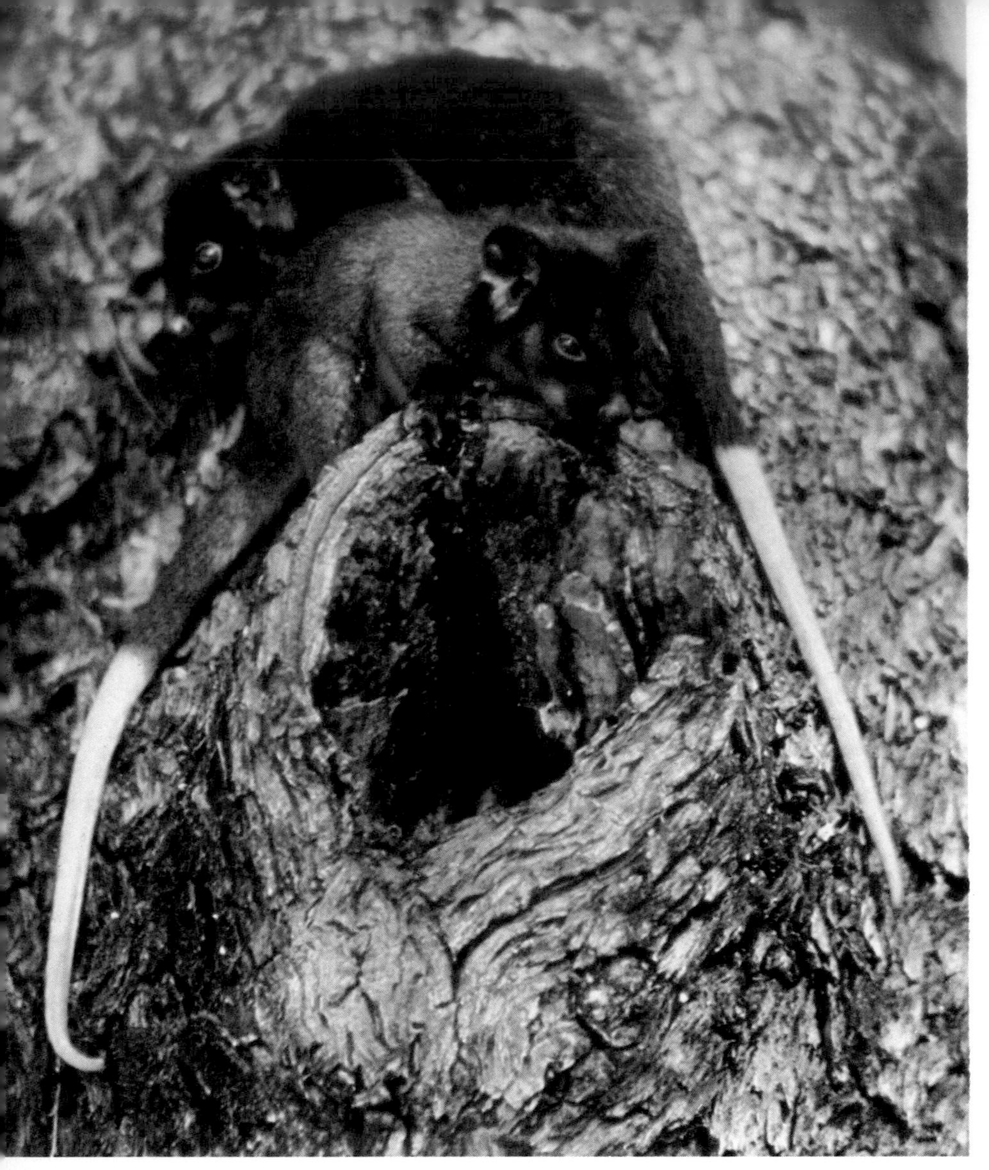

That's what I'm talking about: in this understory level very little can be on the ground unless it's in a hollow log. Most things are up in the trees. Here we've got a nest — not a bird's nest — an animal's nest, and it's peculiar to this peppermint understory.

Mum's left the nest — she's gone up higher, but she's left the children home. Twins. Twin ringtails, a boy and a girl, just big enough to be looking after themselves and for mum to go away and leave them. She's up the top of the tree watching very anxiously. See why they're called ringtails: the lovely long tail is prehensile and curls and twists around when they're up in the trees, hanging on — it makes an extra and useful leg.

The little girl's got a pouch: it's a true mammal, a true marsupial. They eat insects and birds' eggs, frogs, all those sort of things, and they build up their diet with eucalyptus and peppermint leaves. They'll come into gardens and eat flowers and fruit, so they've become quite a pest in town. But their pest quality is nothing when you balance it with the beauty of the animals themselves.

Now they can go up the tree and she'll come down. Any incident like this, any drama, is watched because observation is a main method of survival in the bush.

Everything must survive so every method is used. Bees can sting and there's lots of them here, but some animals are quite innocuous — no bite, no sting — so they use other techniques for survival.

Some of these insects are pretty hard to see: here we have perhaps the best of all the camouflages. He's desperately being a piece of dead grass — he doesn't want to know me because I might eat him. You can't see him? The walking stick or stick insect — a beautiful animal, absolutely perfectly camouflaged. The whole body is attenuated and lengthened out, the colour is the same as dead vegetation and whatever position he goes into he just freezes, and then it's very hard to see him. As soon as I put him down, he finds a new position, and he rocks his body, to give the impression of grass moving in the wind, because even when it's very still, grass tends to move a little bit. So stick insects are perhaps the best of all camouflage experts. They're phasmids — leaf eaters — not praying mantises, as many people might think.

Protection is the name of the game and camouflage stops you being eaten, but it's not the only way you can keep yourself safe. The most common way is to escape. If anything threatens you, move to a safe place. For bird watchers, the most marvellous places are these estuaries and lakes — water birds of all the birds have a special charm for man. They're out in the open, their enemies from land can't reach them because of the water and you can see them. A pelican comes in to land: a beautiful flight, like a Sunderland flying boat. Swans, pelicans and those bobby black and white ones are stilts, White Headed Stilts. Probably a couple of hundred of them in that lot. And on the fence post, a superb White Egret.

Once a Musk Duck goes under water he's pretty hard to follow to see what's happening — but out on land we can use all the technology of the twentieth century to see what the story of life's all about.

Sometimes nests are too high, in very fragile trees, but the rear vision mirror of the car and a bush pole are all you need. Put it up above the nest, look in . . . see the eggs or the young or whatever — but don't touch the nest. We've obviously disturbed Mrs Fantail there — she's very upset. You know the reason why? She saw herself in the mirror and she thought goodness gracious, there's another fantail in my territory, in my nest! So she's really upset about it — where's that other fantail gone? And she's now looking around for the other fantail. So I think I'll quietly leave before she realises it's me she saw.

And here, one of the rarest birds in the world, the osprey — nesting. It's not rare in the sense that you can't see ospreys; it's rare because the pesticides that have been used for agricultural control all over the world have built up as they come down a food chain until the big predators like these ospreys end up getting enormous loads. It either makes their eggs sterile or makes the egg shells so thin that they don't hatch, they crush. By the way these are behaving they've got eggs — the fact that two birds are there and they're both rather anxious about me being here indicates that they've got eggs. If they had young, they'd both go right away ... the young would crouch down in the bottom of the nest and stay there, and the parents would be hunting for food and watching. As soon as I went they'd come in and feed the young. But this behaviour says pretty well: eggs.

One of the marvellous things about Tuart forest is that it contains these very rare things. There's not much forest, but what there is is really worth preserving. While you've got forest, you've got these things too. Lose the forest and you lose them too.

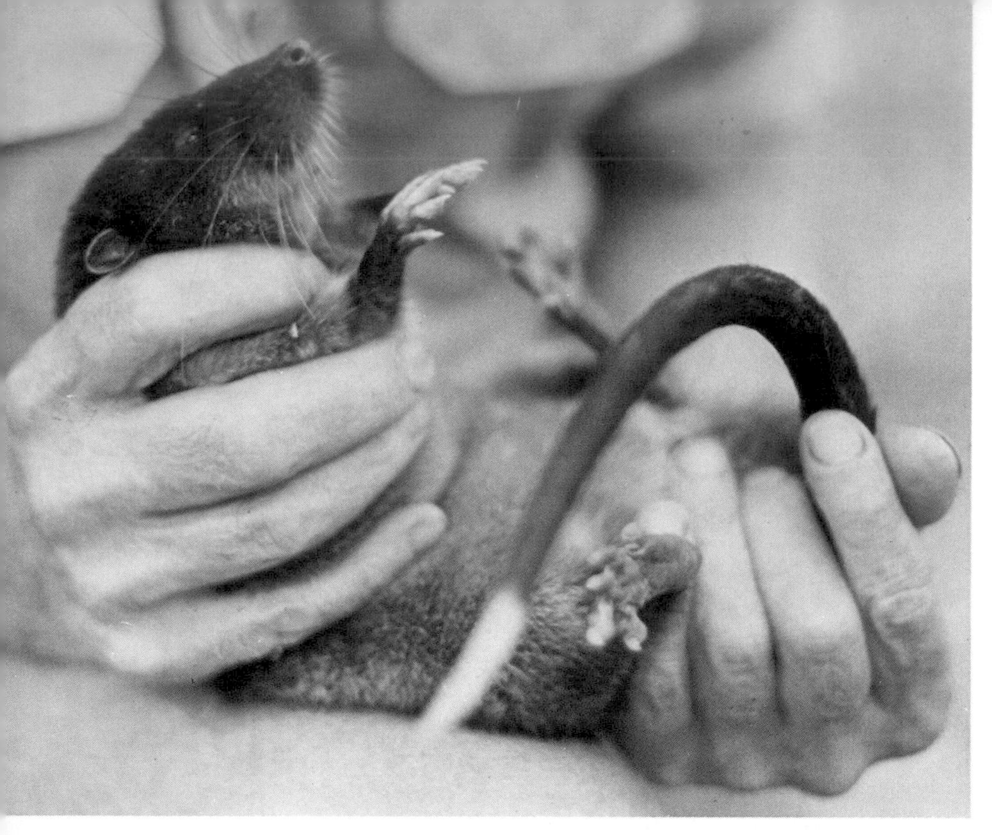

In places as rich as this, every area has to have something living in it. The foxes and cats have cleaned a lot of the ground fauna up, but here we find one of the most beautiful animals in this entire country — it's the Water Rat or Beaver Rat. He's not a marsupial, he's a native rodent. See his big webbed back feet? The front feet are still rat-like for digging. He eats things like crabs, marron, mussels, and swims very, very well. In the water, swimming around, diving down just like a beaver, they come and float on their back in the water, with the mussel on their belly — holding it, eating it, cracking it, like an otter. Mostly they'll come up on the bank and feed on little platforms.

They're an animal that came very close to extinction between 1910 and 1930. The fur is exquisite and, being from a water rat, of course it's waterproof. The fur trade of the world had an enormous demand for the

Australian water rat and they were trapped in their thousands — in every waterway, trappers worked, and the water rats were thinned down and down. And then, about the '30s, there was a wave of revulsion through the ordinary people against the slaughter of animals in the name of beauty — and the conservation movement really began then. So this animal has been able to survive through the beginning of that movement. Look at him go! straight down the bank, into the water . . . a quick nose around and then off across the lake . . . effortless movement . . . really swimming along because he knows where he's going. This is his territory, and because I happened to have disturbed last night's home he's heading across the bank to another house that he's got on that side.

The Tuart forest is always associated with the sea, and with the coastal limestones that are formed by the hardening effect of rain on the coastal dunes. This is the top of the limestone. The lime and the sea winds and the salt all combine to change this area — through enormous pressures on the plants. Each one of these flowers — and there are hundreds here, all different sorts, and shapes and colours, flowering right through the year — each one of them has evolved with this environment; this particular coastal heath, wind-pruned, limestoned, sandblasted, everything, and these plants evolved with it and as part of it.

And with the plants have evolved the insects — the two things have come up together: Australian wild flowers and Australian insects. And when you look around at any of these bushes there's a constant movement of insects coming and going . . . if you watch very closely you'll see that certain ones go to certain plants.

But overriding it all are the bees. Just the common, ordinary garden bee. You see, the bees short-circuit the specialised pollination methods – the relationship between the Australian insects and the plants. Some flowers, for example tube flowers like this one, need moths, not bees. The moths that pollinate these under normal conditions land on the top and their furry bodies pick up the pollen and transfer it from one flower to another; but the bees have found a very cunning way of doing it – they burrow in under the side of the flower, bite through the base of the tube and take the nectar out. So they don't touch the pollinating part at all. And, as a result, long tube flowers have virtually disappeared from this landscape, purely because of the bee selection, and flowers which bees can pollinate remain. That must change the environment.

But there are other ways bees do it too: when the bees run wild, swarm from the hives of the apiarists, they nest in hollows where native animals live. And there's another positive way in which they affect the environment: if a bird or an animal learns to eat bees, learns to handle them like the Rainbow Bird, which beats them in its beak and takes the sting out before it eats them, then that bird has got a big supply of food, so it's advantaged and it builds up in numbers. But whenever something goes out of balance in an eco-system, the whole eco-system goes out of balance. Bees have got a very important role in our agricultural scene – they pollinate clovers and pastures and fruit trees, because they come from the same country. Introduced trees we eat from come from the same area – Europe and the Americas.

But in areas which are reserved for the preservation of the Australian heritage, bees have no place; they have no part. They're alien to this environment and by their very presence they're changing it and we can't afford to have it changed the slightest bit. There are sufficient dynamics in the pressures of nature and climate . . . the pressures of the whole eco-system itself . . . without throwing in these extra factors of bees and all the other introduced beasts like foxes and rabbits and cats – they all cause changes, and we can't have change if we want to keep our Australian bush.

SOUTH-WEST FOREST

jarrah

This is typical Jarrah forest, very much associated with the history of Western Australia. A hundred and fifty years ago the first settlers came to the Swan River Colony, across the coastal plain country to this sort of forest, and it broke their hearts. A vast grey mass, that's the only way you could describe it. Rolling hills, dense trees, thick timber, and more and more timber. The forest extends from just north of Perth to east of Albany. The settlers persisted and hacked out their farms, and even today the same pattern exists of little pockets of farmland in the great forest. But it wasn't really the farms that mattered — it was the forest and the timber that came from it that opened the colony up, and when modern technology came the little mill towns disappeared and now their sites are battlefields — a battle between the native plants trying to take back the land, and the plants that the settlers brought in which are spreading and trying to establish themselves and hold their ground.

These areas with their blend of parkland and bush are naturally places where people come for picnics. They bring their children to this lovely place, and yet this beauty contains all sorts of danger. Old rusty iron and broken glass can harbour anything; you get all sorts of bities and nasties. Here's one who's particularly bitey and nasty to children, a Dugite or brown snake — one of the very dangerous animals in this area. It looks like any other of the common brown snakes in Australia, and is one of the Brown Snake family. This particular type of Dugite is called a Kabarda because of the black spots scattered along his body. Some of the black spots are ticks. He's quite a friendly looking snake but he is one of Australia's killers. The fangs are very short, in the upper jaw. These are quiet, non-aggressive snakes, but if they do get annoyed, they stand and fight. At this time of the year he's just come out from his winter sleep and he's been brewing his poison for a whole winter and so now it is really strong.

How do you tell a Dugite from any other snake? It's under the tail that matters — single scales all the way until you get to the vent, and from there on there's a zigzag line up the middle of the tail. That zigzag line differentiates this snake from most of the others. He's pretty harmless except if he bites you, but he gets out of your way and doesn't bother to chase or attack. Most of these snakes are very quiet and peaceful.

The other thing here is the Redback Spider — just as dangerous as the snake but it doesn't move so fast. Broken tin, broken bottles, snakes, killer spiders, all things which make this particular battleground a very dangerous place in which to be.

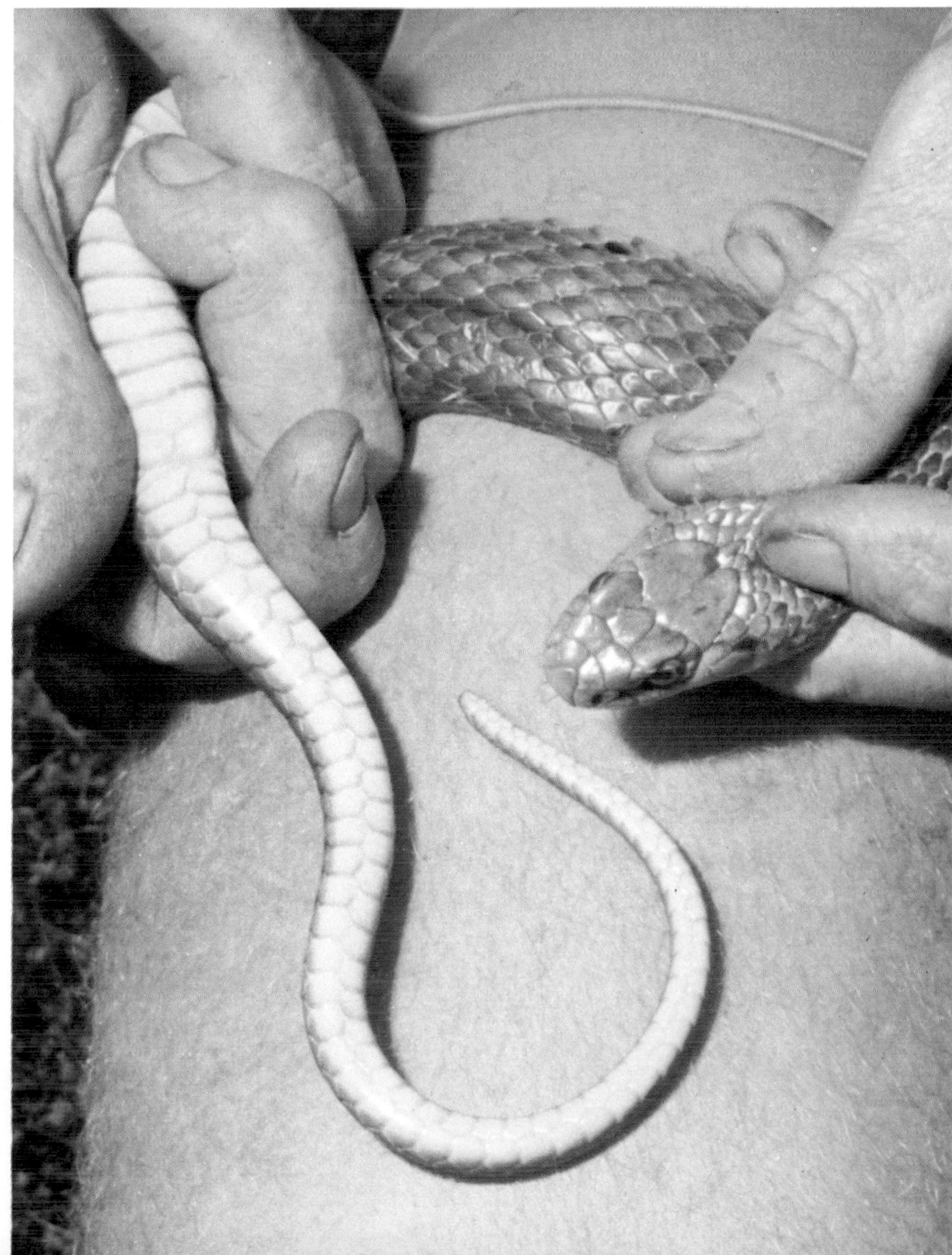

Just across the way is the intact forest. Its original inhabitants include some very remarkable things. One is the Zamia, genus *Macrozamia,* the male plant right alongside his wife, the female plant. The only difference is their fruits, not the number but the type of fruit. The male produces spores and each frond has thousands of spore cups on the back. As these ripen they just spill out on the ground like great masses of white flour. Each female segment has two little fruits attached. These fruits become pollinated by spores from the male and turn red.

In the middle of each red fruit is a nut. When they are dried up the bush rats come and eat the kernels out, leaving the nut hollow. But that's not the end of the nut, because the hollow shell might become a home for another animal, such as a lizard.

These Zamia fruits are a very important food source. Even people can eat them. But they contain a poison which has to be leached out with water. The Aborigines used to eat them by soaking the fruits in a stream and then baking them. They can give cattle a disorder called rickets — so cattle don't come into Zamia country very much. That helps to preserve this area — an area of wildlife refuge in the centre of country which has been developed.

Another fascinating plant is the Blackboy, a sort of lily. Its dead trunk is a good home for many sorts of animals, and one of them is the Bird of Paradise Fly. The male is a little tiny thing like a mosquito, with a bunch of gauzy hairs in his tail. He flies through the forest while the female waits in a hollow somewhere — she's a great big lumbering thing. He comes along to visit her and she gets pregnant. In due course a remarkable thing happens: she turns herself outside-in and lays eggs in a cavity inside her own body, then she dies, and the eggs hatch out.

When I touch one full of hatching eggs it leaves a trace which explains their common name — Mealy Bugs. They're related to the Coccids and the Lac Bugs which produce cochineal and lacquer. The galls you see on trees are produced by other relatives.

You needn't be scared of the Little Whip Snakes, even though they're poisonous. They are called *Denisonia gouldii.* They like to live under a cover of nice cool, wet bark.

Their fangs are too short to penetrate the normal person's skin and their poison is not potent enough to affect humans seriously.

People amaze me. They say, 'Oh, the beauty of the bush!' and they mean only the wildflowers and static things like that. But a beautiful animal like this snake gets a different reaction: 'Chop, chop, chop — kill it as quick as you can!' Flowers are delightful but they're static; these things are far more beautiful and have the added attraction of being mobile.

The kookaburra is probably the best known of all Australian birds, and we use it as a national symbol — yet in this forest it's a killer. It was introduced into Western Australia, and so it's just another exotic animal in the Jarrah forest and it destroys the natural fauna. When I take a handful of debris from the bottom of a nest I find the sort of things that kookaburras eat: beetles, birds, frogs, native mammals — all the little things that live in the forest.

But in the country to which this bird belongs, New South Wales and Victoria, its natural habitat includes a big tree-climbing goanna, the Lace Goanna. The goanna walks around the forest and when it hears the beep-beep-beep of young birds in a nest it climbs up the tree and has kookaburras for dinner. That means there's a natural balance, but in the Jarrah forest those lizards don't occur and kookaburras proliferate and the native animals have no protection against them. They've spread all over the Jarrah country — where it ends, they seem to disappear. They're very interesting and amusing animals, but — oh, dear! What they do to small birds and animals!

Most of the 'snakes' you see caught by kookaburras are actually legless lizards, but people are conditioned to believe that kookaburras kill snakes, and so they think that's what they are seeing. And because people are conditioned to think that snakes are bad, therefore kookaburras must be good. But not here!

Nothing is bad when it's in the right place; few things out of place are good.

A lot of people have the impression that birds will abandon a nest if it has been touched, as you've seen me doing. But if you don't leave a fear scent or a strong man scent in the area, birds will usually come back.

It might seem that the Jarrah has all the enemies there are — beetles and bugs which eat the trees, fires that sweep through, tree-cutters, and one you wouldn't expect — sandhills. These began a hundred years or so ago when the first settlers came and cleared the flats for stock. But they were sand flats and the wind caught and blew the sand and next thing there were rolling dunes — a hundred feet of them sometimes, rolling in and drowning the forest.

The whole forest could become like that without care and conservation. Forestry management works towards helping the relationship of animals, plants and the land.

Even the dune areas have a use in a managed situation. One of the biggest problems facing the Jarrah is the disease called dieback, a fungus disease transmitted mainly on the wheels of vehicles. One of the growing sports is the use of off-road vehicles and dune buggies. The dune area here is a controlled area for the use of these vehicles, so disease transmission is contained. People can enjoy their sport and the forest isn't threatened.

The regeneration program has been successful — you can still see little bits of sand here and there which have been broken up and will soon grow over. The last big dune is being held by Marram grass which works in several ways to hold and transform the sand; it catches seeds which blow on the wind and when they grow into native plants the animals can begin to live on them.

If you get up early, you'll find such tracks as those of the Rat Kangaroo or Woilie. The one I've caught has been in a fight — there are no actual teeth or scratch marks, so it's probably one of her own clan she fought with — a male who's kicked her out of her own area, so she's gone looking for somewhere else and been caught by the first light and ended up in a not very good sheltering log. She'll work her way into it, digging and scratching.

Rat Kangaroos are beautiful animals but very nervous, and this one doesn't like being caught. All the kangaroo family have a split toe which they use for fur combing. The Woilie has a long curved tail which rolls up and is used to carry bundles of sticks to make nests.

In the early days Rat Kangaroos were very common but about 1930 they disappeared — they had formerly been spread as far north as Broome. Today they are starting to re-establish in a few isolated pockets. They fought the problem of the introduced animals, of man and his incursions and his regular burnings, and now they're coming back. This whole area is being worked by a special group of foresters who are studying the wildlife. It's been made a refuge area for wildlife. The animal I've caught will get a tag in her ear — then we'll put her back where we found her. The foresters are able to keep track of the animals, and tagging helps them know what the population is, what they eat, how far they move, how big a territory they need — and, most importantly, what sort of places they need to live. All of that put together makes up wildlife management, and management is the only way we can keep these animals alive.

SOUTH-WEST FOREST

wandoo

Australia is the home of thousands of unique wildflowers. Some are really strange, bizarre plants. In this forest there's a very ordinary one that has a lot to do with conservation: it's the common old 'eggs-and-bacon' plant. This tiny, rather attractive but insignificant-looking plant has saved the whole forest, and with it a great range of Australian animals.

'Eggs-and-bacon' is a poison plant, *Gastrolobium,* which kills stock. Therefore the first settlers who came to this area found the easy-to-clear forest was not available for running stock — the problem of getting rid of the poison plant was too much.

It's got a special relationship with other wildlife, too. The flowers produce little black seeds which are eaten by the Bronzewinged Pigeon. The pigeons store the poison in their bone marrow; predators like foxes and cats who eat the Bronzewings die of it. Quite a turnup! That hated poison plant is responsible for saving the native animals in this area. Wandoo forest is found on the dry edge of the winter rain area of south-western Australia. It forms a superb open forest, and the timber is very dense and hard, giving it a high commercial value. Mixed with the open forest are other sub-stories, or independent habitats, such as mallee, mallet (which is used for tanning), *Gastrolobium* (the poison plant), carpets of wildflowers, open grassland — altogether there are something like 4000 species of plants living here.

There are areas in which the Blackboys grow. It's one of the most graceful and beautiful plants in this part of the forest; its called *'reflexa'* because of the way the skirt turns downwards.

The spines are very sharp and when you're walking through the bush they can be quite dangerous at eye level. The turned-down skirt consists of dead leaves, and underneath them all sorts of animals find homes. When bushfires occur the dead leaves burn off and their bases form a beautifully insulated protective mass.

Eventually the Blackboys die, as all things must, and it's the dead Blackboys which make the most interesting homes for animals. They're insulated outside,with a soft core inside which has been eaten out by grubs, and that's where many animals live.

It's in one of them that I find something interesting. By following up some fresh marks of scratching and digging I discover a pair of Gould's Wattled Bats. They don't like sunlight, so their eyes are closed, but they have their mouths open to show their defensive teeth — which don't hurt, because they're insect-eating teeth.

When you've examined an animal like this, and enjoyed it, you put it back where it came from. That's what conservation is all about.

Unlike humans, most animals work at night. They're nocturnal, and spotlighting is a useful technique in animal observation. A bright light makes their eyes reflect and you can identify the various animals moving about. You never know what might turn up next.

Did you ever see such a fat frog as this one? It's the Spotted Burrowing Frog and he's out after the moths and insects which are around at night. He swells up as a protective device: if a predator comes along the frog immediately puffs himself up with air to twice his ordinary size, which makes him seem very hard to swallow. Then he squirts out a sort of milky fluid on his back — it's a burning poison. He's a burrowing frog, and has enormous back feet with shovels built in. On the front foot there's a lovely claw. His great big eyes reflect back the spotlight beam. The frog, or toad, is very sluggish and slow; most things can catch him, but because of that poison he's pretty safe from attack.

The granite outcrops here are ancient — some scientists say they are seven hundred million years old, the very bones of the earth. They are being changed by the climate, breaking down to soil. The run-off of water from them encourages the growth of she-oaks, which like the extra water and the sandy soil.

In the hot southern summer this kind of rock heats up, and when the rain falls, or the nights get cold, the rock cracks off in great flaky sheets — which make magnificent homes for animals.

A couple of skink lizards are living here. They're sluggish — it's been raining and they must warm up again. They're Egernia Skinks — pleasant carnivores who run around the rockfaces eating cockroaches and other insects.

You can pick up any rock here and find something living under it. Under one, the find is: a Redback Spider, cockroaches, another little spider — and the owners of the hole, a couple of Bobtail Lizards, a male and a female. The male has a long, skinny tail; the female a short, fat tail.

People have a nonsensical idea that their bite is poisonous. They can have a good bite at me, but I won't die. The teeth are so short that they only mark my skin. They are related to the Bluetongue, another skink lizard.

Next find is a Carpet Snake, hunting here for lizards. It's a beautiful snake: all snakes are beautiful, but some are more beautiful than others, and these are so placid and wonderful that you could really have a love affair with one.

They're Pythons — typical ones. They have a very ornate pattern of small scales which gives them their name of Carpet Snake — from the old-fashioned Brussels carpet pattern. They have fairly long, stout bodies, big heads and small necks. They're not poisonous. One of the interesting things about them is their back legs: it's really just a scale, the remnant of what was once a leg, because they evolved from walking animals to gliding ones.

When he moves over my hand it's like silk flowing. They're not cold or slimy — they're beautiful animals, one of my favourites.

All around this area there are birds — the Brown Tree Creeper, for instance. Here there's a young one waiting to be fed. Even at an early age he's able to run up the tree trunk without problems. Tree Creepers are specialists in their diet — they eat ants, so there's plenty of food available here.

There's something else that's not a bird, though it does lay eggs. It's something special — probably the most primitive mammal in the world, except for the platypus. It's the Echidna or Spiny Anteater. As soon as he sees me he goes into his defensive position — but the poor fellow's got one problem: his hind claws are so well developed for digging that one has to stick out. If you touch one it retreats, but the other one has to poke out, so you can get a grip on him. It's the one weakness in his protection against foxes and dingoes and other predators.

He has a lovely long nose and seven inches of tongue. He's out hunting for termites: most mammals here come out at night, but this one's an exception. He comes out in the afternoon and goes termite-hunting, scuffling around in little bushes looking for the termites which live just under the surface. He digs with his powerful claws and then . . . slurp! Seven inches of instant death goes up the tunnel and zaps the termites. He eats about three or four thousand of them in a day.

His back claw is very long for obvious reasons: how do you scratch yourself if you get an itch under all those prickles? That long claw is for getting in among the spines and having a good old scratch, because he gets ticks and lice the same as other things do in the bush.

He's threatened by one of our introduced animals, the fox, who's learned a way to handle Echidnas. The fox comes along, the Echidna sees him and rolls up in a tight ball. The fox will roll him with his nose to a pool of water, if there's one handy, and as soon as he hits the water the Echidna unrolls to start swimming and — zap! The fox has got him, because the belly underneath is soft and unprotected.

The animals of this forest rely for their survival on the management of the forest area, the control of burning and the retention of ground litter. The entire eco-system is interdependent and only management can save it.

The Numbat is just the sort of animal that this management program is about. He's the official symbol of the Wildlife Department of Western Australia, and the symbol of the conservationists in their fight to preserve vanishing animals. His only relative has already vanished from the desert country . . . the Rusty Numbat, which must have looked very much like this one.

The remarkable thing about this animal, which is related to the native cats, is that it's got more teeth than any other marsupial in Australia – about 54 of them. Yet they never bite. When you catch them they're completely quiet and passive. They're quite magnificent.

It's animals like this that the conservation movement is about. People really like animals; they – and their kids – want to see them. The best thing we can do is preserve the habitat and so preserve the animals.

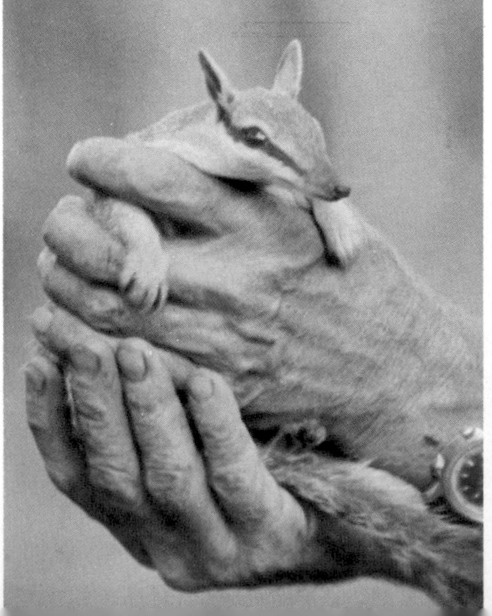

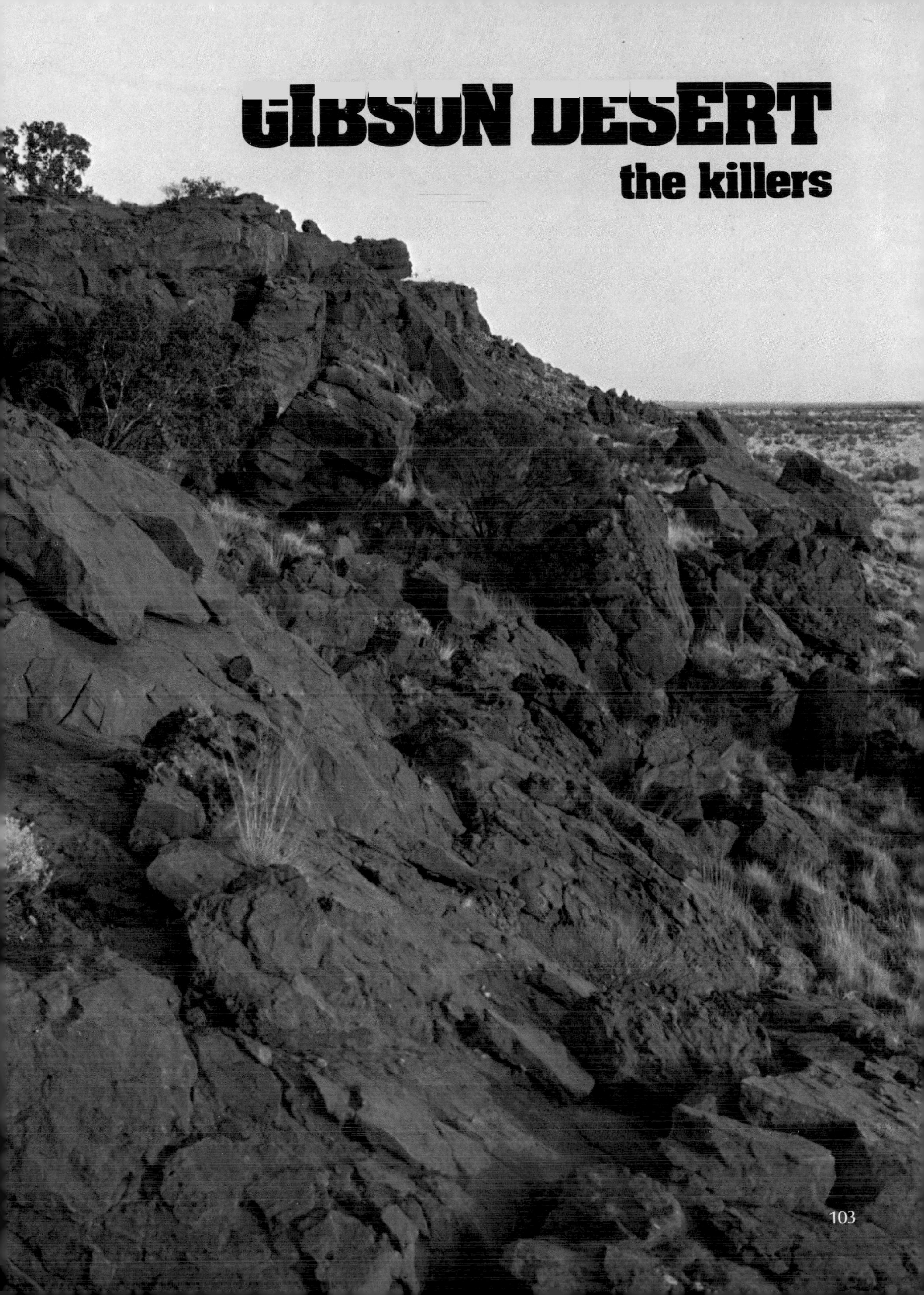

GIBSON DESERT
the killers

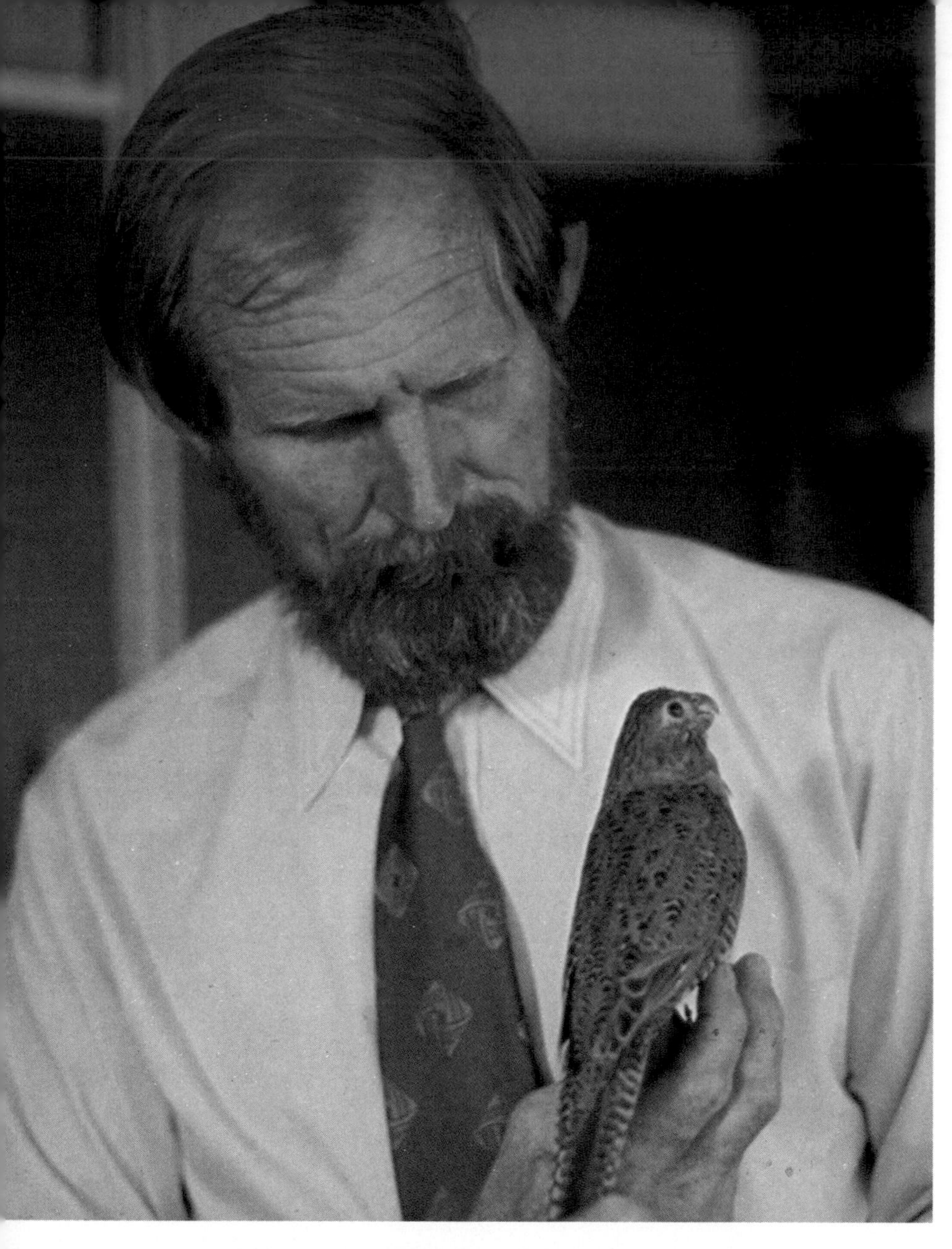

Mammals are very special animals to humans: they're soft and furry and cuddly so the extinction of a mammal seems more significant than the loss of a reptile or a bird. And more than twenty Australian native mammals have become extinct since the coming of the pioneers. You'll find them only in museums.

Then again, nobody has seen a Sticknest Rat in Western Australia for perhaps eighty years, though they still exist on Kangaroo Island. The little Marl, a beautiful small desert bandicoot, seems to be gone: no trace for seventy years.

It's quite obvious that the white man is responsible, but you can't blame it on hunting — the Aborigines hunted these animals for food, and the animals survived. So it's something to do with the way we live — the white man's lifestyle has done it. If we go out as far as we can, away from the influences of the white man, perhaps we'll find some answers to why these things vanish.

So we head for one of the harshest environments in the world. Out here you have to be totally self-sufficient — you're dependent on what you have with you, because the environment won't help.

The most intriguing of the vanishing animals known to have lived in this environment is the Night Parrot, and I'll head for the most remote waterhole in this desert country — because if the Night Parrot still survives, that's where it's going to be.

Travelling in this country you must have broad tyres on your vehicle to get through the sand — and being soft-walled, they're easily punctured by any little stake you encounter, so progress is slow and tiresome.

My destination is Durba Springs in the Durba Range, but it's not readily found on a map — it's on the southern edge of Lake Disappointment. The sun is beating down, brassy and glaring; the whole countryside is quivering. There are no living things except plants — trees and spinifex, mile after mile of nothing very much.

The endless rolling sand dunes here are a mystery: the experts still haven't decided how they are formed. Some think they're formed by the wind rolling across them, others that they're formed by the wind running down their length. Here and there are even more desolate patches of stone or gibbers or salt lakes. The whole area is unprepossessing and empty. And yet, when you look, there's life here — even in this hottest part of the day.

Along the tops of the dunes is the refuge area for animals; they dig their burrows there to escape the heat. And because camels, in particular, use the dune tops as a highway, they're being eroded and the refuge areas destroyed. The running sand filters into the burrows and chokes them. Plants roll away, there's nowhere for seed to lodge and the whole thing becomes a wasteland where nothing survives.

A Sand Goanna (or Gould's Goanna) is digging for his breakfast. Working on the scent of food, he ignores my presence and just keeps on digging, completely unafraid.

Food is a very important aspect of survival even for a reptile that can live for a long time without the sort of replenishment that we have to have every day.

The *Moloch horridus* is the most beautiful ugly animal in the desert. The aborigines call him 'Mingari' — from *'minga'*, meaning ant — and he's an ant eater — you've never seen anything eat until you've seen him eating ants. He eats three thousand or so at a meal, licking them up one by one, and getting enormously fat on it. He's also known as the Mountain Devil. He was called *Moloch horridus* because Moloch was a devil in the Bible, and the first scientist to see him said, 'What a horrid devil!'.

He hasn't much of a tail; his main bulk storage is in the fat body and in a peculiar little bump behind the neck — it's something like a camel's hump. Excess food in the form of fat goes into it. It looks like a false head — and whenever a Mountain Devil gets really alarmed he puts his head down and the false head sticks up.

He's completely harmless unless you sit on him, because his prickles are quite sharp — or the points are; otherwise they're quite soft and flexible. Mountain Devils are typical dragon lizards in that they change colour to suit their environment and their mood: if they're feeling happy they're lighter in colour. And if a lady Mountain Devil happens to wander by, they get brilliantly coloured up. The one I've found *is* a lady, and that tummy is not all fat — there are probably six or seven eggs in there and she's probably looking for a good place to dig a burrow in the sandhill and lay her eggs. So I'll treat her with the respect she deserves as a pregnant mum and put her down.

Considering the drought and other factors that are affecting this environment just now, it's a wonder to find any living things at all. Yet certain animals are so well adapted that they exist even under these harsh conditions. Like flies, for example!

The only thing ground animals can't hide is their track, and one track leads me to the mouth of a burrow. In it lives the Kurdaitja Lizard, or Knob-Tailed Gecko. In Aboriginal folklore the Kurdaitja is the secret assassin, and this lizard is supposed to come along at night, when you're asleep, and if you're a man it crawls up your leg and removes the bits of you that make you a man, so you end up not being a man any more. It's not true, of course!

You'd wonder how an animal as fragile and delicate looking as this could survive in this harshest of harsh environments. He uses every trick. The mouth of his burrow is very small, and he comes out at night; in the daytime he pushes the dirt from inside the burrow back up, closing the mouth, leaving just the tiniest of breathing spaces. There's a series of baffles to stop the hot air coming in, and he burrows deep. The burrow is always under the edge of a little bush or something, to get the effect of the available shade.

The animal itself is remarkable: he has great big eyes for nocturnal vision, with huge overhanging brows which push the sand away from his eyes when he's burrowing. He has a ridiculous little tail: we don't really know what the tail is used for: but whatever it is, it must be for a very good purpose. The knob on the end might be a lure for insects, or for sexual attraction, or for some other purpose.

We must bear in mind that animals are governed by the need for food, or protection, or sex – and every aspect of an animal has to relate to one or more of those things.

When we reach the beginning of the Durba Range we still have a long way ahead of us.

Around the edge of the claypans and gibbers here you find a few stunted shrubs surviving on the run-off water. This range is really a great saucer of rock with high edges, dipping towards the centre. Any rain which falls is collected in the saucer and channels out through a few well-defined gorges. It's in the gorges, because of the water and the soil, that big trees can grow. Once the water leaves the range and reaches the sandhills it's lost forever, disappearing in the endless desert.

It's a surprise to come across a traditional oasis in Australia — complete with date palms, which are totally out of place in our landscape. We do have native palms, but not this sort. These were the result of drovers coming down the stock route, eating dates and dropping the seeds.

If both male and female palms appear, they can cross-pollinate and there will eventually be groves of date palms around waterholes like this. People not aware of the delicate environmental balances might think 'Oh, good!', but bear in mind that these plants have no relation to the Australian environment. Animals out here have not learned to adapt to them: they might eat the fruit, and insects might eat the pollens — but this is a piece of Australian environment and any introductions are bound to be harmful in terms of the original things here. It would be a tragedy if they took it all over.

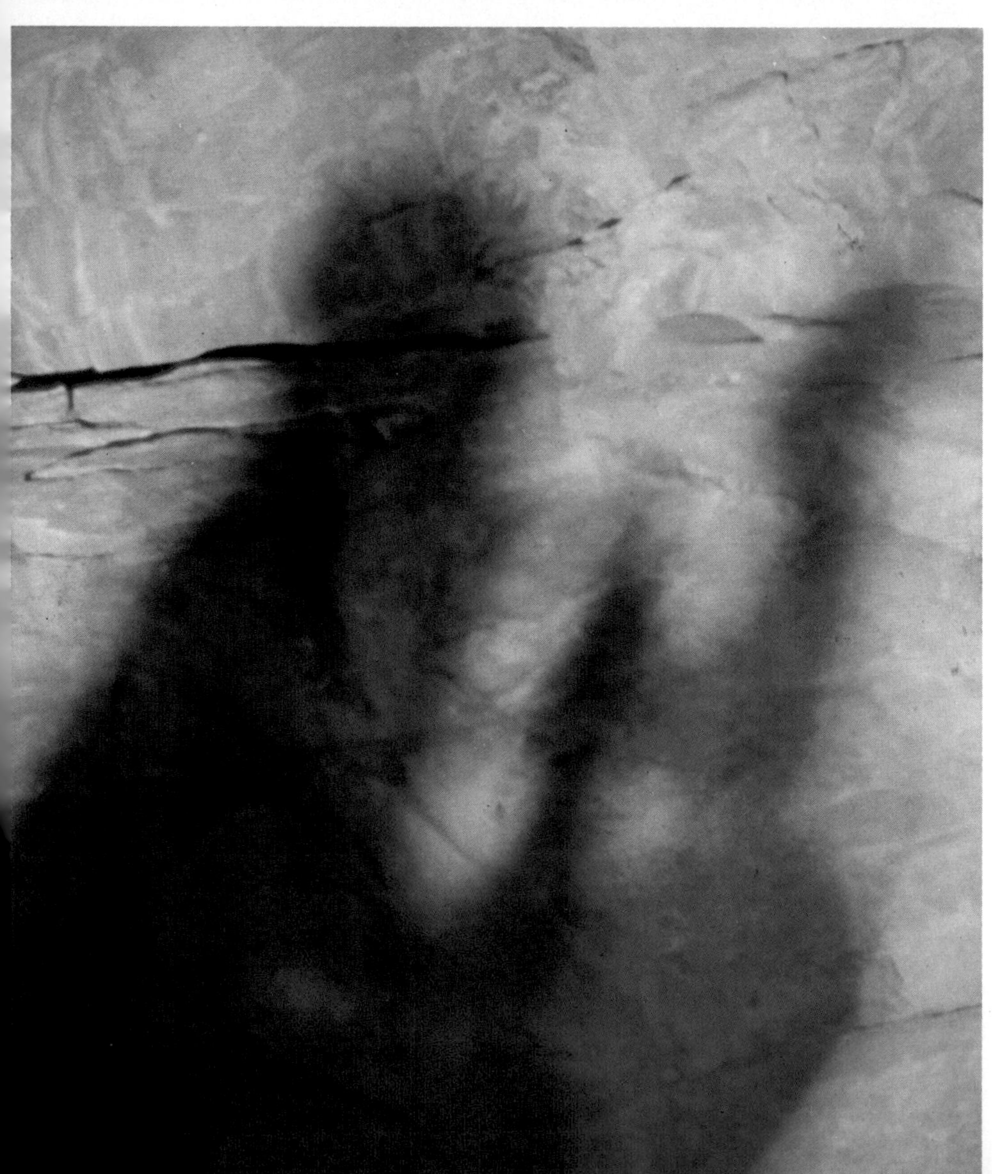

After three hundred miles of sandhills, a pool of permanent water is a beautiful sight. Lying at the foot of a great gorge, it has a green scum that looks urky, but means in fact that it's good water. The green comes from living things, so it's not a dead pool. It's a hub for all the animals and birds which depend on it as a drinking place. That's why I'm here — and it's the only place I can survive too.

One of the first things you notice about this magnificent place is death; bones, skulls and feathers wherever you look. Life and death seem to go hand-in-hand here. Death has even come to one of the killers — a cat. He's succumbed to the same problem as everything else — lack of food. He's actually eaten the waterhole out: by constantly preying on it he's cleaned out virtually everything here, and what's left he's been unable to catch, so he's died.

Another dead relic is what's left of a fox. The evidence suggests that he's been caught by a dingo. It's an odd situation: an introduced animal which is hunting, smelling around the waterhole to catch birds and things, being in turn caught by a dingo.

Those two are clues to why this beautiful place, which should be teeming with the life it can sustain, is nothing but desolation. I was hoping to find the Night Parrot here — but with introduced predators in the area, it seems unlikely.

At the end of the day, like thousands and thousands of men before me in this place, I'm sitting by the most basic of man's tools — the fire. You can imagine what it was like perhaps 200 years ago at this time of day. The fires burning, the Aboriginal people sitting around, the children waiting, knowing this was their time of day. A warrior or an old man starts to tell the story about this place: about Waaru the Rock-Wallaby. He acts his part with his shadow on the rock-face — the Rock-Wallaby comes down, he stops, he looks about, he hops on again, coming closer, closer ... and the mimicry is so perfect in the flickering light that the man is no longer a man, he's a wallaby, and the children's big eyes are staring in wonder.

The whole way of life for these people was thus woven into the fabric of their religion and belief — food, water, shelter, life and death!

This place must have supported thousands of people in time through the animals and birds that came to the waterhole. Yet today when you look around, there's hardly a trace of any animal here. And the big question is: why? Why in such a short time, a scant hundred years or less, have all the native animals gone? Why is there nothing here?

Not quite nothing — first light brings the phenomenon known as 'the dawn chorus'. That's when you find out what birds are still in the area. But these are all birds commonly found over all desert country in Australia: the things which have vanished are the rare and beautiful desert dwellers. And they seem to have gone for ever.

I'll set up a mist net — a net so fine that it's hard to see. Its purpose is to catch birds, in this case the Night Parrot, if it's still around. If it is, it's going to have to come to this waterhole to drink, because this is the only one in this vast desert area. My chances are pretty thin — there's a thunderstorm kicking up, and if it rains the birds, if there are any, will spread all over the desert, living on the little bits of water everywhere.

Why do I hope to catch the Night Parrot? It's simple — for about a hundred years he hasn't been seen. This is one of the most remote areas in Australia — there are no stations, just this waterhole and miles and miles of spinifex desert . . . and the Night Parrot eats spinifex seed. I'm hoping to prove it's not extinct.

There have been eighteen months of dryness, and all the little waterholes have dried up. There's an excellent chance that, if the parrot still exists, this is where he'll be drinking.

But the weather's caught up with me, as it always does when you plan something. The rain comes down, and that's the end of the expedition. With all this water all over the desert, there's no chance. All this fuss over a little green bird about eight inches long, that looks like a fat budgerigar!

This magnificent place is virtually dead, when it should be teeming with life. The reasons are obvious: cats, foxes, camels . . . and man. Their pressure on this one small oasis has reduced the numbers of the things that relied on it until they went down below the level of reproduction . . . and now they're no more.

The old people who lived here knew it to be a wonderful place. Now their understanding and trust in the land has been shattered with their culture.

GIBSON DESERT

some survive

The usual scene in the Australian outback — birds, late afternoon sun; the tank, the trough, the cattle yard, and in the centre of it all the windmill. It's the core, the heart of the whole enterprise of this outback country development. Would you believe this very symbol of success in this country is also the symbol for death and destruction for native fauna and for the whole Australian environment?

Number nine well on the Canning stock route, 1600 kilometres north-to-south from Hall's Creek to Wiluna. A very important place, particularly this number nine well, for historians, naturalists and pastoralists. Its real importance is that this place, once a very important watering place for the Aborigines, is the extreme edge of the pastoral country. Beyond here is desert, not used by white man; the other way is exploited land, so this is the edge. And this edge effect could give us some answers to why so many of the animals in this apparently untouched country have vanished forever. Apparently it's untouched, but this country carried thousands of cattle in a good season, even though at the rate of only one cow per hundred acres or thereabouts. So you see, there's a lot of land hereabout.

You drive through to Meekatharra on a good sealed road that serves the cattle country and the mines, then it's beef road out to Wiluna, and from there a desert track to No. nine well.

What a mess! Last time I was here it was quite different. There was just a spring, the tank didn't exist, the windmill was here but as part of the spring. All of this destruction is the result of the use of the land. In a good season it's okay — but now it's over-used. All of the cattle that normally spread over a thousand hectares in this vicinity on little tiny waterholes have now come in here. The little holes have all dried up. Why did the owner put a tank in? For that very reason! When the dry season comes all the cattle walk to this water. It's all downhill and they make their pads and tracks, and they eat out the vegetation — and as soon as the rains come, the water washes soil down, fills the water holes up, fills the springs up, and there is no water. So, to save the cattle, the tank is built and that causes the death of many of the native animals.

Sweet, good water, is the basis of life for over half the animals in this area — but also the basis of death. If you had the time you'd sit, quietly here by the tank, and you'd see all the birds that do drink come in during the day and drink. But from this very drinking comes their own destruction. You might argue that this permanent water supports an enormous number of birds. True -- but the birds that drink water are seed-eating birds primarily, and they can only fly a certain range around here. They're in direct competition with the cattle and the sheep for plant food — so what happens is that all of this country is eaten and trodden out, bared and blown with wind; the seed is gone and each day the birds have to go further and further out to food, and then back to water. Suddenly the time comes when they can't make it, and then they die. Under normal circumstances even if everything did die it wouldn't matter because nature would replenish them from the survivors in the surrounding areas, but everything dies here in a bitter drought, at the last refuge. Everything dries up and blows away, the rains come and the first animals back are the introduced stock because they're brought in by man. Man's own improvements again caused the total destruction of the area.

It's almost a complete contradiction in terms. Water, the very essence of life to us being the thing that destroys animals. Not very pretty, is it? Wherever you go in this harsh country, death is commonplace.

Because of the proximity of the waterhole and the general lack of cover in this area even the most casual observer can see big game and get quite close to them because of their weakened condition, but the art of the naturalist is to see the less obvious. Once your eye is in, once you know what you're looking for and how to look, there are signs of small life everywhere, even in this completely desolate area. There's a little stump with a burrow going into it; there's a rock with a burrow going under it. One animal can own a whole area, something like a territory, and he'll move around and feed at night time — the cool time; that's part of his survival technique. When daylight comes he goes into the nearest hole. All these burrows belong to the same animal, and to find him you usually dig them all out. In this case he's been a bit unlucky — he must have been getting in late and he's left tracks so we know he's under *this* one.

He's pushed the dirt up behind him to stop the hot air going down the burrow after him. He's a member of the Gecko family. A very attractive animal, who can't stay in the sun for too long — it's enough to kill him. They come out at night, and for cover in the daytime they can utilise holes in the ground or bark, or even cow droppings as long as it's enough for insulation. They eat insects, things like termites which also utilise all the little sticks and the cow droppings, so there's a whole wealth of food and it's nice succulent juicy food. They don't lose water; every time we breathe out we expel a certain amount of water — so do other mammals — but lizards don't do it. Cold blood means that their body temperature adjusts to the air temperature around them and once they get down into the ground where it's cool they cut down food intake so when a dry time comes, if they go down far enough, they can stay for a long time. So geckoes, in spite of their very fragile, gentle appearance, are really very fine survivors.

If we pull a log over we find a Burrowing Skink — a lizard that's on his way to becoming legless, as some lizards are. His method of protection is his colouring. From above or the side he looks the same as the ground. His legs are reduced to almost nothing to help his wriggling in the loose sand. He has a great long tail which is full of stored food. His eyelid has a transparent disc in it which allows him to burrow through sand and not get grit in his eyes. He needs to seek the maximum amount of cover — the temperature in the sun will dry out an animal like this in something like ten or twelve minutes, and that means he'll be dead.

To investigate *this* hole we need a special technique. First we pour in some water; the burrow wanders around under the ground, so we dig along the path the water follows to find the owner of the hole. It's a scorpion — a female by the size of her and ready to lay eggs. I hold the dangerous part in my fingers — the claws don't matter; she can use them to nip but they don't hurt me at all.

This scorpion could make you sick for one or two days if it stung you; the really bad one in this country is much smaller than this, and it's been known to kill people. But scorpions are one of the over-rated dangers of the outback.

You might think that because I've destroyed the burrow that it will be the end of the animal, but not so. All I need do is put the soil back and the animal will work its way out tonight and be quite okay.

The popular concept of desert is empty sand wastes. Australia is mostly desert, but our deserts are quite different; stony gibbers, salt flats, sand and rock. The sort of rock here is the greatest reservoir of wildlife in the whole desert area — it's called breakaway and it's got everything. Of all the desperate areas in this desolate landscape the worst is the tops of these breakaways; the water runs off, the wind howls across — and yet there are still things living here.

This little bush, a mulga, has almost died dozens of times in its three hundred years of life – it's been *bonsai'd* by the extreme elements. Its cousins down on the flat, where conditions are good, are 20 feet high; but up here the struggle is such that this one will never get any bigger. If it did the wind could get under it and flip it over, and it would die.

A lovely smell! Australian Sandalwood – a stunted little tree that grows right across the dry country. It formed the basis of an enormous trade between the Orient and Australia in the early days because its wood was very valuable. People came, pulled the trees out with horses and left only the little plants. But the leaves are very succulent, so the cattle eat them, and so do sheep. Sandalwood trees bear a fruit – a nut – which used to be the staple diet of the Sticknest Rat. Because this is rocky country and because there's Sandalwood here, it's very likely there are Sticknest Rats in the area – or were at one time.

In the desert Spring the first animals to move are the big carnivorous reptiles. One is the Perentie, the 'pontewey' of the Aboriginal people. It's a goanna, and it sleeps through the cool part of the year. It's shedding skin which is badly infested with ticks which got on to him during the dormant period. He hasn't started to eat yet, so he's fairly skinny.

It's a noticeable thing about this landscape that it contains so many reptiles, specially adapted to the desert conditions because of their cold blood. For the half of the year when the temperatures are cold they're away in hiding; their period of activity is the other half of the year. The hotter it gets, the faster they get — up to a point. But there is a lethal temperature for each animal; the goannas have the highest range of all, but when it gets too hot this fellow would probably find his way to a water trough or a spring or a pool. He'd plunge in and lie with just his nostrils sticking out. When the heat is really on, the caves are the final refuge for the animals of the desert.

There's a cave here that looks as though it might have been a dingo's lair. There are chewed bones — and owl pellets. These pellets are the bones and fur of animals which the owls have eaten . . . then thrown up. There's the skull of a native rodent, the bones and skull of another, the jawbone of a marsupial mouse, bits of tiny carnivores like small native cats. I'll take all of this material back to camp to sort it out.

Imagine getting enthusiastic about owl pellets! And yet I am. To a scientist, they're interesting; that's a bandicoot jaw — and no bandicoots have been seen in this country for something like ninety years. And one very ordinary piece of bone, from its size and shape, can belong only to a Sticknest Rat. When you add that to the chewed Sandalwood nuts found occasionally along the breakaway it suggests one thing, the possibility of that animal still being here seems pretty high.

So it's important for me to do two things; get hold of all those owl pellets, and look for a Sticknest Rat.

Being a naturalist is a lot of hard work, but every now and then you get a break — in this case it's clues to an animal thought to be extinct.

And finding a nest, which seems to have been in use within the past five years, means that a report must go to the Museum. Investigation and survey of the area can tell us whether the animal is still alive or not.

GIBSON DESERT

death of a waterhole

The centre of the Outback – a glorious place where it all comes together! It's nothing special that would even show up on a map – but there are sandhills and mulga and rocks, the whole essence of the Outback.

It's not a hostile place, just totally indifferent to people and animals and to life itself. But if you know how to use it – and every surviving plant and animal out here does know – then it's a very pleasant place.

Australians have built up a sort of mystical feeling about the Outback, a sort of folk-culture idea which like most such ideas has some basis in truth, and a whole lot of nonsense in it. As with people, the Outback bush is what you make of it!

Here you'll meet the Mulga Snake or King Brown, as he's known over most of Australia. This one's only a prince – he's half grown. He's easily told from all the other bities in this country by the peculiar pattern on the underside of the tail. It's not a good idea to go around checking them this way to see what they are because this is a killer, or at least a potential killer. Up here it does no harm. At this time of day he's just off home to bed, having had a good evening's hunting, slept through the cold of the night, and been brought out by the warmth of the morning sun to have a final hunt around for a grasshopper or a lizard. Then he'll hole up for the day and come out again about 5 p.m. to start feeding again.

When I say 'feeding' – that's pretty difficult to do in a country which has very little food to offer, so his main ability is to use this very lack of food – he can go without for enormous lengths of time.

In captivity, I've had such animals which refused to eat for twenty months, and then suddenly – three mice in a row! Normally, they'd eat about one every month or even less.

When you get over your fear of them snakes are very lovely animals, but of course they *are* dangerous. Yet even the dangerous ones have a place in the system, out here where they can do no harm to anyone.

This apparently empty country is rich in history: a history of exploration and of exploitation. It's the furthest out that man's exploitation has taken place – right on the edge of the great desert heart of Western Australia, the Gibson and Sandy deserts.

John Forrest's fort was built here; he was probably the first white man in the area. His party came up here in the late 19th century searching for new areas for development in the colony of Western Australia. That was before Federation – it was still a colony. John Forrest and his brother were remarkable men, for colonists: they had a lot of respect and feeling for the Aborigines – and the only time on record that Forrest was ever attacked by Aborigines came right here.

He wrote in his diary something like, 'We made camp in this pleasant place and suddenly over the hill came a horde of plumed and painted savages, and we reluctantly had to fire over their heads until they ran away. Then we built a fort.' This has always puzzled me because Aborigines were never 'plumed and painted' except during ceremonies, and Forrest was very careful about trespass and tried to understand their ways.

When I came here and looked around the facts became clear. I believe this was sacred ground, as shown by the stone circles, and Forrest had unwittingly stumbled on a ceremony.

The Forrest party was the first through here, but about the same time came a number of other groups – people like Giles, Warburton, Carnegie, great names in Australian history. Carnegie summed up the whole area as 'a howling wilderness of spinifex and sand'. Unfortunately nobody believed him: the others happened to come through in good seasons and put in glowing reports. This was good country, they said; potential stock country. The pastoralists moved in, bringing herds, and the Canning Stock Route evolved.

This stock route, created to move cattle from northern to southern Australia, is really one of the greatest achievements of the Australian pioneers – and the monument to the achievement is a series of 80-foot holes in the ground. They are really the monument of the most remarkable desert traveller of the whole area, Canning himself.

Wherever he sank one of these holes in this desolation, he got water – and that *is* a remarkable feat in this waterless land. Canning's job was to build a cattle trail from the Kimberleys to the markets of the south. That meant that the wells had to be one day's travelling apart – in bad country 12 miles, in good country maybe 20. And each well had to be exactly the same. Why? After a full day's drive in the dust and heat, with one white drover probably riding behind and the black boys coming ahead, the system had to be simple and uniform.

A horse pulled a rope that went around a pulley and down into the well; the bucket came up, the water was tipped into a wooden gutter and ran into the troughs where the cattle would drink when they caught up.

The structure needed timber of a size that doesn't grow in the area, but clever carpentry allowed them to use the local wood – beefwood or desert oak. There was also a small windlass for emergencies – in case someone came along on foot and needed water in a hurry. They used bloodwood, mulga and desert oak for that.

Another killer of the area – a beautifully efficient one – is the Collared Sparrow Hawk. Usually they kill things like finches and budgerigars, but here he's attacking a Spotted Bower Bird. The Bower Bird fights back, but it's no use. To some people the sight of this bird eating a living victim seems cruel and unnecessary, but it's part of the struggle for existence: only the strong can survive, and the weak therefore must die.

We move on to what must be the most desolate, inhospitable, unpleasant, unbelievable, shocking place to live that anyone could imagine. It's like a great snowfield or a tundra, but it's really a salt lake, Lake Disappointment — and a ruddy good name for it, too! As far as you can see is mirage, with nothing to suggest that there might be anything else in the world. If you dig you'll find only salt water.

Yet animals have managed to adapt themselves to living here. Animals from the surrounding country, if they happen to be blown or wander on to here, die unless they can get off it. But within this wasteland of strange forms and bubbles of gypsum and salt, certain animals live. There's an ants' nest, and probably next to it will be a spider's nest. Spiders eat the ants, ants eat the insects that wander out here, and on the edge of the lake live lizards which very bravely make dashes out here and grab the spiders in the evening and early morning.

The unwary could die in this boggy salt environment — but it's natural, nature's way of destruction. Destruction is far more brutal when man steps in and is a direct, uncaring cause of it.

Winditch Spring is a permanent body of water in country that would break anybody's heart — cattleman, naturalist, Australian — when you see it in the dry season. Anything living in this area will be around the water.

Five years ago the water stretched a mile and a half, but it's shrunken now. It used to be surrounded by reeds and bulrushes, but they've mostly been beaten and eaten out of existence. The spring is under pressure from an enormous number of cattle, who have come from all around to this one remaining waterhole and eaten it out.

It's still good water, even with a few dead kangaroos and other beasts in it. The flow of the spring is so great that it keeps relatively sweet, even with cattle churning it up. There should still be a few things surviving in this environment, even now.

Some animals, such as the red kangaroo, are helped by the development of pastoral leases, and animals like the goanna which feed on dead things are also on the increase.

Native animals are very dainty in their drinking: they don't churn up the mud, they drink carefully, looking about them in the cautious and aware manner that helps them survive — observation for survival.

The last time I was here the then much bigger pool had some remarkable animals, survivors of a much wetter period. We can still find the Dinner-Plate Tortoise, which exists only in these isolated inland waters. They are one of the Snake Tortoises — their heads go sideways into the shell — Australian tortoises are like that. He has clawed web feet, and a great big mouth with little tiny nostrils up on top of the head, so when he goes underwater just the tip of the nose needs to be showing and nothing can get him.

This waterhole is important because it's a last refuge: if the creatures here disappear, they're gone forever. The last time I was here there were about 50 tortoises, a whole little colony. They won't breed at this time of the year, but when the floods come again with the rains the tortoise will laboriously climb the banks, dig a hole and lay 15 to 20 eggs. The foxes will come and dig up the eggs, and crows will come and eat them, but eventually some young tortoises will hatch out and immediately scurry to the water. On the way the goannas, the hawks and everybody else will have a feed off the young tortoises. A few survivors will make it successfully.

Since each tortoise lives about 50 or 60 years, it's just as well that too many don't survive — otherwise we'd be overrun with tortoises.

The slime on their backs is part of their camouflage. When you dive to look for them and swim along the bottom among the weed, the only thing that shows is the heads looking up — then they'll suddenly panic and start scrabbling, and little clouds of mud float up. That's how you know where they are. When you release them, they go straight back to a safe place among the weed.

Most people like cows, and yet they are the innocent cause of catastrophe. All of this bare grey plain was once lush, thick bushland, with tall river gums, wattles and plenty of other trees. Then the cattle came. They first of all eat off the grasses and the ephemerals; then they graze on the young plants and trees as high as they can reach. The result is that the shadow which normally keeps the ground cool around the trees is lost, and no part of the ground under the trees is in shade all the time. This bakes the ground, causes higher evaporation and cooks the shallow roots of the trees.

The survival mechanism of the trees then triggers the drought response, which is to drop surplus leaves. These would normally cover the ground beneath the tree and stop the loss of water by evaporation. But the cattle eat the dropped leaves, or they blow away, and the trees die. Then the trees are uprooted and blown away and the whole country becomes a bare plain with just a few of the bigger trees left — and when they die nothing replaces them at all.

Another part of the problem is the tracks made by the cattle on their way to drink. Their hooves churn up the ground to dust, the rain carries the dust into the waterhole and silts it up — so there is less water for the animals. Just the amount of water they drink is yet another problem — a large herd drinks an enormous amount of water each day, leaving less for the wildlife.

The lack of trees causes higher evaporation — and so on until all the problems together add up to destroying the waterhole. And when it's gone, everything else goes too.

So there is the problem: how do we maintain a pastoral industry as well as the wealth of wildlife and the natural heritage which is so peculiarly Australian?

There are some not terribly expensive answers. All the waterholes can be fenced wherever they occur. It's a fairly cheap proposition: a windmill would pump the water up on to a flat and the cattle would drink there at a trough. Why? Why not just let them drink here? What does it matter? We've got all these millions of hectares of land — why should it matter if a waterhole dies?

You can cut off a man's arm or his leg and he'll still live; if you cut out his heart he'll be dead. This is the heart of our country.

There's so little of it, it's so precious, it's our heritage and we can't afford to throw it away for the sake of a little bit of temporary gain.